Preface

Let's be realistic about vocabulary study. Learning words cannot guarantee you admission to college or propel you toward automatic success. But knowing the meanings of important words can be useful. If a word you don't understand keeps cropping up in your reading, you must stop to look it up or sacrifice understanding of the text. If you find yourself having to make do with a general word like *nice* or *pleasant* because you don't know a more specific word, you may feel frustrated and your speaking and writing will lack precision.

Vocabulary study, therefore, can be of value to you if the words you learn are commonly used in the kind of reading you'll be doing or will help you say what you mean in more interesting ways. Learning the meanings of obscure words may make you feel sophisticated but will do little to enhance your ability to read and communicate.

VOCABULARY 5 is a book that avoids the pitfalls of teaching obscure words. It presents words that have use in the real world. It requires that you learn only two words per lesson and furnishes you with what you need to know about using the words.

After reading the explanatory matter, you confront two kinds of practice with the new words. In the first kind of practice (Exercise A), you test your ability to *recognize* the meanings of the words as you must do when you encounter them in reading a magazine or a newspaper article. In the second kind of practice (Exercise B), you test your ability to *recall* the words and use them in the proper way. This practice prepares you to use the new words in your own speaking and writing. Words from previous lessons keep showing up in the practice exercises, and so you never have a chance to forget them. By devoting ten minutes a day to this kind of vocabulary study, you will take command of approximately two hundred useful new words as well as hundreds of synonyms and antonyms of the vocabulary words.

But that's not all. As a bonus, this book includes lessons that introduce you to over forty Latin and Greek word parts on which several hundred English words are based. Learning these word parts will give you the keys to the meanings of countless other unfamiliar words.

Lesson 1

surmise (v) (sər-ˈmīz)

ORIGIN: Latin *supermittere* (to throw upon)
MEANING: To think or to infer without having strong evidence
CONTEXT: "Since it was raining hard, I *surmised* that my sister's family from out of town would be late for Thanksgiving dinner."
SYNONYMS: suppose, suspect, imagine, guess, presume

bungle (v) (ˈbən-gəl)

ORIGIN: Unknown; perhaps from the Swedish *bangala* (to work ineffectively)
MEANING: To do something clumsily and awkwardly
CONTEXT: "In spite of careful instructions, Earl *bungled* the job."
SYNONYMS: mishandle, botch
ANTONYMS: succeed, triumph
OTHER FORMS: bungler (n.), bunglingly (adv.)

A. Circle the letter of the best meaning for each vocabulary word.

1. surmise: a) mishandle b) sermonize c) suspect d) dislike
2. bungle: a) dig b) botch c) suspect d) break
3. surmise: a) suppose b) put down c) read quickly d) laugh
4. surmise: a) promise b) guess c) noise d) plea
5. bunglingly: a) carefully b) loudly c) blunderingly d) slowly

B. Supply the proper form of the most appropriate vocabulary word.

1. Martha O'Hara, fearful that the inexperienced intern might __bungle________ the job of bandaging her hand, insisted on waiting for Dr. James.
2. Mrs. Green would not permit her four-year-old son to help repaint the kitchen for fear he would __bungle________ even the simplest tasks.
3. The shopkeeper __surmised________ that the vandal who had smashed the display window might be the lanky boy who usually loafed around the playground.
4. Sharon __surmised________ that Michael might invite her to the movies when he waited for her after play rehearsal.
5. The inexperienced sailor __bunglingly________ loosened the wrong line, allowing the boat to drift away from its mooring.

Lesson 2

fastidious (adj) (fa-'stid-ē-əs)

ORIGIN: Latin *fastidium* (disgust)
MEANING: Showing or demanding excessive delicacy or care; hard to please, critical
CONTEXT: "He is such a *fastidious* housekeeper that every weekend he spends hours mopping, dusting, and cleaning."
SYNONYMS: particular, meticulous, finicky
ANTONYMS: tasteless, uncritical, sloppy
OTHER FORMS: fastidiousness (n.), fastidiously (adv.)

cower (v) ('kau̇-[ə]r)

ORIGIN: Icelandic *kura* (to mope)
MEANING: To crouch in fear or shame, act afraid
CONTEXT: "The man *cowered* before the police who had stumbled upon him in the alley."
SYNONYM: cringe
ANTONYMS: attack, assault, retaliate

A. Circle the letter of the best meaning for each vocabulary word.

1. cower: a) imitate b) elevate c) cringe d) conceal
2. fastidious: a) careless b) particular c) skinny d) quiet
3. cowering: a) defying b) guessing c) cringing d) talking
4. bungle: a) play b) mishandle c) lead away d) guess
5. fastidiousness: a) clumsiness b) meticulousness c) tastelessness d) intelligence

B. Supply the proper form of the most appropriate vocabulary word.

1. Ann ___cowered___ before her angry father.
2. When the sales representative continually referred to her manual of company policy, the customer ___surmised___ that she was new to the firm.
3. The ___fastidious___ secretary neatly hung her coat on the hanger, quickly wiped off the slight layer of dust which had settled overnight on her desk top, and restraightened the pile of papers on her desk before knocking on the boss's door.
4. The defeated nation ___cowered___ before the enemy, too weak to halt their advance.
5. After the worker ___bungled___ the job of repairing the precious family clock, the irate owner complained bitterly to the repair service.

Lesson 3

marital (adj) (′mar-ət-l)

ORIGIN: Latin *maritus* (married)
MEANING: Of or relating to marriage
CONTEXT: "The young man moved from a small apartment to one large enough for two when his *marital* status changed."
SYNONYMS: nuptial, matrimonial
OTHER FORM: maritally (adv.)

martial (adj) (′mȧr-shəl)

ORIGIN: Latin *martialis* (of Mars, the Roman god of war)
MEANING: Relating to war or to the military life
CONTEXT: "We can assume that the ancient Romans were a *martial* people because of their many wars."
SYNONYMS: warlike, military, bellicose, belligerent, militaristic
ANTONYMS: civilian, peaceful
OTHER FORMS: martially (adv.), martialism (n.), martialist (n.)

A. Circle the letter of the best meaning for each vocabulary word.

1. marital: a) warlike b) belligerent c) matrimonial d) mistaken
2. martial: a) called up b) married c) military d) nuptial
3. cower: a) cringe b) disguise c) question d) invent
4. fastidious: a) critical b) lovely c) righteous d) noisy
5. marital: a) blissful b) married c) warlike d) hard

B. Supply the proper form of the most appropriate vocabulary word.

1. Dreams of ____ marital ____ bliss begin with an engagement ring.
2. The taxes you pay to the federal government depend in part on your ____ marital ____ status.
3. The fascist party adopted ____ martial ____ uniforms that conveyed the military spirit of their organization.
4. The ____ fastidiousness ____ of Dutch immigrants was apparent in their spotlessly clean homes.
5. ____ Martial ____ law was imposed on the city to prevent further rioting.
6. Since it was snowing heavily when I got up this morning, I ____ surmised ____ that school would be called off.

Lesson 4

swab (v) (swȧb)

ORIGIN: Low German *swabber* (mop)
MEANING: To clean; to apply medication
CONTEXT: "The nurse *swabbed* the wound with an antiseptic solution before applying the dressing."
SYNONYMS: wipe, mop, clean
OTHER FORM: swab (n. meaning "a wad of absorbent material")

condone (v) (kən-'dōn)

ORIGIN: Latin *condon* (grant)
MEANING: To disregard or overlook something illegal or objectionable
CONTEXT: "I cannot *condone* his rude behavior even though I understand the reason for it."
SYNONYMS: excuse, pardon
ANTONYM: condemn
OTHER FORMS: condonable (adj.), condoner (n.)

A. Circle the letter of the best meaning for each vocabulary word.

1. martial: a) matrimonial b) forgiven c) militaristic d) similar
2. swab: a) borrow b) clean c) overlook d) wound
3. condone: a) excuse b) punish c) confuse d) wipe
4. marital: a) belligerent b) enlisted c) nuptial d) primitive
5. condonable: a) fastidious b) presumed c) excusable d) debatable

B. Supply the proper form of the most appropriate vocabulary word.

1. Mr. Williams, Phillip's teacher, ___swabbed___ iodine on Phillip's cut knee.
2. Some job applications still contain questions about ___marital___ status, that is, whether the applicant is single, married, or divorced.
3. Although the local gambling club contributed large sums of money to civic projects, the new mayor firmly refused to ___condone___ its activities.
4. The frightened seven-year-old child ___cowered___ before the gang of older teens who menacingly approached him on the playground.
5. The emergency medical unit badly needed a fresh supply of ___swabs___ for cleaning the wounds of the disaster victims.
6. Although the psychiatrist did not ___condoned___ the young girl's behavior, she worked painstakingly with the child to help her understand her impulses to steal.

Lesson 5

compatible (adj) (kəm-ˈpat-ə-bəl)

ORIGIN: Latin *compatibilis* (sympathetic)
MEANING: Capable of existing together in harmony
CONTEXT: "Since I never hear them disagreeing or quarreling among themselves, I would say they are a *compatible* couple."
SYNONYMS: congenial, congruous, suitable
ANTONYMS: incompatible, unharmonious
OTHER FORMS: compatibility (n.), compatibleness (n.), compatibly (adv.)

foyer (n) (ˈfȯi-ər)

ORIGIN: Latin *focus* (hearth)
MEANING: An anteroom or lobby
CONTEXT: "We visited with friends while we waited in the *foyer* of the theater for the performance to begin."
SYNONYMS: vestibule, lobby, anteroom

A. Circle the letter of the best meaning for each vocabulary word.

1. compatible: a) unlikely b) harmonious c) amusing d) talkative
2. foyer: a) fold b) hallway c) lobby d) awning
3. compatibility: a) dislike b) animosity c) briskness d) congeniality
4. marital: a) discordant b) matrimonial c) warlike d) savage
5. compatibly: a) hardly b) awkwardly c) mistakenly d) harmoniously
6. foyer: a) telephone booth b) anteroom c) trick d) crease

B. Supply the proper form of the most appropriate vocabulary word.

1. Because their computer system is ________ with ours, we could easily link the two into one large communications network.
2. The ________ was jammed with theatergoers during the play's intermission.
3. Susan O'Neill is a fastidious contractor who would not ________ the use of inferior construction methods in order to complete the hospital addition ahead of schedule.
4. Before giving a transfusion, blood types must be checked for ________.
5. The doctor ________ the boy's badly skinned knee with antiseptic cream.
6. "The registration desk and information center are located in the ________ of the hotel," explained the bellhop.

Lesson 6

Dilemma · Wrest

wrest (v) (rest)

ORIGIN: Old English *wraestan* (to twist)
MEANING: To gain with difficulty by, or as if by, force or violence
CONTEXT: "They have spent their lives *wresting* a meager living from that rocky farm."
SYNONYMS: wring, wrench, extract, extort
OTHER FORM: wrestle (v.)

dilemma (n) (də-'lem-ə)

ORIGIN: Late Greek *dilemmat* (involving two assumptions)
MEANING: Any perplexing or difficult situation or problem
CONTEXT: "Last night I was in a *dilemma* over whether to stay home and wait for Jane's call or go to the concert and hear Lisa play."
SYNONYMS: predicament, question, difficulty
ANTONYM: certainty

A. Circle the letter of the best meaning for each vocabulary word.

1. foyer: a) intrigue b) foil c) aisle d) anteroom
2. dilemma: a) answer b) predicament c) solution d) ignorance
3. wrest: a) hit b) wring c) push d) recline
4. martial: a) nuptial b) bellicose c) matched d) happy

B. Supply the proper form of the most appropriate vocabulary word.

1. Whether to be loyal to one's personal values or to those of society can be a perplexing moral dilemma.
2. After overcoming the robbery suspect in a dangerous struggle, the police were able to wrest the pistol from him.
3. Because they were basically not compatible, the couple quarreled continually.
4. When the demonstrators protesting the MX missile were not admitted to the main offices of the Pentagon, they waited in the foyer until they could voice their complaint.
5. "I could not wrest any meaning from that obscure, poorly written essay," complained the frustrated student.

wan (adj) (wän)

ORIGIN: Old English *wann* (gloomy)
MEANING: Lacking color; suggesting ill health or fatigue
CONTEXT: "Jane's *wan* face flushed with pleasure when she saw the bouquet."
SYNONYMS: pale, pallid, ashen
ANTONYM: ruddy
OTHER FORMS: wanly (adv.), wanness (n.)

spinster (n) ('spin[t]-stər)

ORIGIN: Middle English *spinnestere*
MEANING: A woman unmarried beyond the usual age of marrying
CONTEXT: "Our nearest neighbor is a *spinster* who has lived alone ever since her mother died ten years ago."
SYNONYM: old maid
OTHER FORMS: spinsterish (adj.), spinsterishly (adv.), spinsterhood (n.)

A. Circle the letter of the best meaning for each vocabulary word.

1. spinster: a) loom b) widow c) old maid d) problem
2. wan: a) small b) pale c) frisky d) embittered
3. wrest: a) implant b) relax c) extract d) tire
4. dilemma: a) mistake b) perplexity c) worry d) fear
5. wan: a) ashen b) willowy c) stumbling d) decreased

B. Supply the proper form of the most appropriate vocabulary word.

1. The father was worried by his lethargic child's ____wan____ complexion.
2. Instead of ________________ before the midnight intruder, the normally timid dog lunged viciously at the dark shape.
3. The middle-aged ____spinster____ lived quietly in a huge, ramshackled house with two hounds and a Saint Bernard dog.
4. The government, desperate to secure information about the guerrillas, ____condoned____ the use of force in interrogating members of the movement.

Lesson 8

secrete (v) (si-ˈkrēt)

ORIGIN: Latin *secretia* (separation)
MEANING: To release, discharge, or generate some material
CONTEXT: "The salivary glands in the mouth *secrete* saliva that starts the digestion of starch."
SYNONYMS: excrete, eject, emit
ANTONYMS: receive, absorb
OTHER FORM: secretion (n.)

vagrant (n) (ˈvā-grənt)

ORIGIN: Latin *vagari* (to wander)
MEANING: Someone without permanent employment or a home
CONTEXT: "Observing the shabbily dressed stranger wandering aimlessly around the town, the police assumed that he was a *vagrant.*"
SYNONYMS: vagabond, wanderer, tramp
ANTONYM: resident
OTHER FORMS: vagrantly (adv.), vagrancy (n.)

A. Circle the letter of the word in each group that does not belong.

1. a) discharge b) emit c) secrete d) absorb
2. a) tramp b) resident c) vagrant d) vagabond
3. a) careful b) fastidious c) finicky d) sloppy
4. a) vagrant b) resident c) homeowner d) settler
5. a) eject b) release c) secrete d) reveal
6. a) secretion b) discharge c) ejection d) confusion

B. Supply the proper form of the most appropriate vocabulary word.

1. Bile is a substance ________________ by the liver and used in digestion of fats.
2. Because he had been up studying all night, the boy's face was ________________.
3. Although the local steel factory was desperately in need of workers, the ________________ preferred to spend the day wandering about town.
4. The rebels were unable to ________________ control of the government from the hands of the rich landowners.
5. The sweat glands ________________ varying amounts of water daily.

Lesson 9 *Guessing Meaning from Context*

"May I borrow your *whatsit*?" Ed asked. "I need to correct a mistake in this problem, and the *whatsit* on my pencil has worn all the way down."

Anyone listening to Ed would probably know immediately what he wants to borrow. Since the thing on a pencil most often used to correct errors and in the habit of wearing down is an eraser, we can be almost sure that that is what Ed is asking for. The process by which we discovered the meaning of *whatsit* involves the use of *context clues.*

Often, this process is almost unconscious: We are reading an exciting story or article and encounter an unfamiliar word. If context clues are effective enough, we may not even have to pause in our reading but may plunge eagerly on, having absorbed the meaning of what, in isolation, might have been a completely strange word.

Some context clues are so obvious they need little explanation. Direct definition is sometimes provided when the author of the book knows that the reader will probably not understand a new or unusual term. The author places a definition of the strange term right in the text, setting it off by commas or parentheses. For example:

The *tachometer,* a gauge that tells the driver how many revolutions per minute an engine is making, can be found on every good racing car.

Restatement is a similar device in which the explanatory material is introduced with a signal such as "in other words," "that is," "to put it another way," and "or" followed by a synonym:

Mayor Lehrman saw this plan as a *panacea* for the problems that plagued the city; that is, she considered it a cure-all and urged its passage by the city council.

Other context clues are more subtle and may require the careful rereading of a passage in order to find hints about the meaning of a new word.

Examples are often helpful. They usually follow a signal word such as "for example," "such as," "such," "like," and "this." The careful reader will sometimes be able to add up the information in the examples and gain a fairly good understanding of the unfamiliar word. Notice the use of examples in this passage:

Organizing the boys camp was a *herculean* task, requiring that Ted devote hours to such activities as carrying cross-ties for building a footbridge, clearing the area of small trees and underbrush, and putting a new roof on the cabin.

In clues of contrast, the structure of a sentence or paragraph shows that an unfamiliar word is the opposite of a familiar word or phrase.

Although the patient needed a thorough examination, Dr. Johnson had time to give only a *cursory* one.

Exercise: Examine the context clues in the following sentences carefully in an attempt to determine the meaning of the italicized word. Circle the letter of the best guess of the meaning for the italicized word. Do not use a dictionary.

1. The young monk soon learned that *mundane* activities such as scrubbing corridor floors, weeding gardens, sorting mail, and washing dishes were a part of monastic life.
a) unnecessary b) earthly c) religious d) disgusting

2. In deciding which contributions to use in the literary magazine, you should establish a *criterion,* or standard, against which to measure them.
a) set of entry rules b) board of judges c) committee whose task it is to decide an important issue d) a standard on which a judgment can be based

3. The actress's role demanded that she run the *gamut* of emotions from gay frivolity to morbid depression.
a) quick change b) entire range c) gradual decline d) limited number

4. My grandfather is always quoting some old *adage* such as "A penny saved is a penny earned" or "Honesty is the best policy."
a) prophet b) expert c) wise saying d) almanac

5. Most people think Dana is open about her reasons for doing things; however, I know she often has *ulterior* motives.
a) selfish b) important c) impatient d) hidden

6. Jan's biggest problem is *inhibition;* this irrational restraint keeps her from doing many things she would enjoy.
a) unchecked impulse b) internal check to free activity c) willingness to do improper things d) depression

7. Slamming out of the house, Juan shouted that he would never be sorry for what he did, but he returned an hour later, *contrite* and apologetic.
a) hungry b) weeping c) extremely worried d) deeply repentant

8. An *opiate* such as heroin or morphine can be medically useful but socially harmful.
a) medicine b) narcotic c) large plant d) stimulating beverage

Using Context Clues in This Book: In addition to giving you a way of guessing the meanings of unfamiliar words, a knowledge of context clues can help you work the exercises in this book. In the sentences in Exercise B, from which vocabulary words have been omitted, you should be alert to the context clues that indicate what word is to be supplied. It is important that you read the sentences carefully, keeping in mind the various kinds of clues that can help you determine which word to place in the blank.

Also, you will be required to write sentences using the vocabulary words you have learned. You should provide enough clues in your sentences to indicate that you understand the meanings of the vocabulary words. For example, it is not acceptable to write: "My mother is *fastidious,*" because the sentence indicates nothing about the meaning of the vocabulary word. A better sentence would be: "Because of the care with which she cleaned the oven and refrigerator, I could tell Mrs. Taylor was a *fastidious* housekeeper." What kinds of context clues are present in the second sentence?

reprimand (v) ('rep-rə-mand)

ORIGIN: Latin *reprimenda* (to check)
MEANING: To rebuke severely, especially in a formal way
CONTEXT: "The principal *reprimanded* the sophomores for their childish behavior at the assembly program."
SYNONYMS: censure, condemn, reprove, upbraid
ANTONYMS: praise, honor
OTHER FORMS: reprimand (n.), reprimandingly (adv.)

aesthetic (adj) (es-'thet-ik)

ORIGIN: Greek *aisthanesthai* (to perceive)
MEANING: Having to do with beauty or what is beautiful
CONTEXT: "By the appreciative way Allen handled the lovely wood carvings, I could tell he was a very *aesthetic* person."
SYNONYM: artistic
ANTONYM: inartistic
OTHER FORMS: aesthete (n.), aesthetical (adj.), aesthetically (adv.)

A. Circle the letter of the best meaning for each vocabulary word.

1. reprimand: a) forgive b) condone c) return d) upbraid
2. aesthetic: a) insane b) fastidious c) artistic d) athletic
3. reprimand: a) mistake b) condemnation c) compliment d) bride
4. vagrant: a) mourner b) weaver c) gossiper d) tramp
5. secrete: a) absorb b) tie down c) discover d) emit

B. Supply the proper form of the most appropriate vocabulary word.

1. The ________________ were like migratory birds, leaving the city in late fall for a warmer climate and returning again in the spring.
2. The collector extolled the ________________ qualities of the primitive art done by the people of the Sepic River Valley in New Guinea.
3. The boss ________________ the newly hired clerk for making a costly blunder.
4. The ________________ design of the modern building won praise from critics and architects alike.
5. To ________________ a child three days after a misdeed is not effective discipline.

Lesson 11

reprieve
equivocal

reprieve (n) (ri-'prēv)

ORIGIN: Perhaps Old French *repris* (to take back)
MEANING: A temporary relief from or suspension
CONTEXT: "Students were granted a *reprieve* from compulsory study hall until after rehearsals for the play were finished."
SYNONYMS: respite, delay, postponement
ANTONYMS: enactment, condemnation
OTHER FORMS: reprieve (v.), repriever (n.)

equivocal (adj) (i-'kwiv-ə-kəl)

ORIGIN: Late Latin *aequivoc* (ambiguous)
MEANING: Having two or more possible meanings
CONTEXT: "I'm uncertain as to where he really stands because of his *equivocal* answers to my questions."
SYNONYMS: ambiguous, uncertain, questionable, indeterminate
ANTONYMS: unequivocal, certain, definite
OTHER FORMS: equivocate (v.), equivocally (adv.), equivocation (n.)

A. Circle the letter of the best meaning for each vocabulary word.

1. equivocal: a) loud b) definite c) beautiful d) ambiguous
2. reprieve: a) punishment b) postponement c) tax d) ambiguity
3. wrest: a) box b) shout c) wring d) wear out
4. compatible: a) unhappy b) congenial c) silent d) frustrated
5. reprieve: a) respite b) talent c) expulsion d) sorrow
6. equivocate: a) determine b) foretell c) answer d) talk ambiguously

B. Supply the proper form of the most appropriate vocabulary word.

1. The mayor's ________________ answers did not give reporters the information they sought.
2. The defense attorney, convinced that her defendant was innocent, fought incessantly to persuade the governor to grant a(n) ________________.
3. The Senate's ________________ of the senator for unethical conduct severely damaged his chances for reelection that fall.
4. Critics raved about the ________________ qualities of proportion and balance in the architect's latest design.
5. The ________________ from the president's office did not arrive; therefore, all sororities and fraternities on campus were forced to curtail initiation activities.

Lesson 12

rigor (n) (ˈrig-ər)

ORIGIN: Latin *rigor* (stiffness)
MEANING: Strictness, or severity of weather, living conditions, or law
CONTEXT: "The public adjusted to the *rigors* of wartime and did not object too much to the food and gas rationing."
SYNONYMS: inflexibility, stringency, austerity, exactness, harshness
ANTONYMS: flexibility, softness, leniency, compliance
OTHER FORM: rigorous (adj.)

gesticulate (v) (je-ˈstik-yə-ˌlāt)

ORIGIN: Latin *gesticulat* (having made mimic gestures)
MEANING: To make use of gestures (movement of hands, body, or head) to express an idea
CONTEXT: "As the mime *gesticulated*, the audience followed his ideas as well as if he had spoken."
SYNONYMS: gesture, motion, pantomime, signal
OTHER FORMS: gesture (n. or v.), gesticulation (n.)

A. Circle the letter of the best meaning for each vocabulary word.

1. equivocal: a) easy b) certain c) timid d) ambiguous
2. rigor: a) rigging b) strictness c) tremors d) nerves
3. rigorous: a) harsh b) tired c) long d) vigorous
4. gesticulate: a) chew b) motion c) speak loudly d) build
5. reprieve: a) answer b) condemnation c) delay d) honesty
6. gesticulation: a) gesturing b) digestion c) growth d) stringency

B. Supply the proper form of the most appropriate vocabulary word.

1. The ________________ of life in the isolated mountain area contrasted sharply with the comfort and wealth of the nation as a whole.
2. To add emphasis to her words, the debater ________________ energetically as she spoke.
3. The snow fell without any ________________ for eleven days, stranding the villagers.
4. The mere thought of the teacher's ________________ discipline prevented students from creating trouble at recess.
5. Although we could not hear the speaker from our seats in the back of the auditorium, his ________________ made it clear he felt strongly about his topic.
6. The deaf can learn to communicate through the use of ________________.

pert (adj) (pərt)

ORIGIN: Latin *apertus* (open)
MEANING: Lively and sprightly, bold, impudent
CONTEXT: "The faces of the *pert* children charmed everyone."
SYNONYMS: vivacious, flippant, forward, saucy
ANTONYMS: retiring, shy
OTHER FORM: pertness (n.)

consummate (v) ('kȧn[t]-sə-,māt)

ORIGIN: Latin *consummare* (to complete)
MEANING: To bring to completion or perfection
CONTEXT: "It is expected that all plans for the conference on off-shore drilling rights will be *consummated* by Monday."
SYNONYMS: fulfill, accomplish
ANTONYM: begin
OTHER FORM: consummate (adj.)

A. Circle the letter of the best meaning for each vocabulary word.

1. pert: a) portioned b) lively c) respectful d) perfect
2. rigor: a) sail b) brightness c) rudeness d) strictness
3. consummate: a) ruin b) believe c) finish d) insult
4. gesticulate: a) retire b) motion c) eat d) graduate
5. consummate: a) perfect b) full c) gray d) flawed

B. Supply the proper form of the most appropriate vocabulary word.

1. A(n) ________________ smile brightened the face of the four-year-old girl when she spotted the licorice on the shelf in the supermarket.
2. Kevin's ________________ was contagious, making his friends bright and lively.
3. Prior to the Olympic Games, the French ski team led a(n) ________________ life characterized by vigorous exercise, strict diet, and no nighttime entertainment.
4. The skilled potter ________________ his work by applying a glaze to the ceramic bowl.
5. The ________________ movements of the Russian dancer held the audience spellbound as he glided gracefully across the stage.
6. The exaggerated ________________ of the comedian turned her serious statements into playful satire.

Lesson 14

plausible (adj) (ˈplȯ-zə-bəl)

ORIGIN: Latin *plausibil* (deserving applause)
MEANING: Appearing reasonable or worthy of approval; believable
CONTEXT: "The teacher permitted Judy to turn in her theme late because Judy had a *plausible* excuse for not having it finished on time."
SYNONYMS: believable, credible, reasonable
ANTONYMS: implausible, incredible
OTHER FORM: plausibility (n.)

convalescence (n) (ˌkȧn-və-ˈles-n[t]s)

ORIGIN: Latin *convalescere* (to grow strong)
MEANING: The gradual recovery of strength after an illness
CONTEXT: "The doctors say the mayor's *convalescence* will be long but that he will ultimately be as well as ever."
SYNONYMS: recovery, recuperation, healing
ANTONYM: relapse
OTHER FORMS: convalescent (adj.), convalesce (v.)

A. Circle the letter of the best meaning for each vocabulary word.

1. convalescence: a) relapse b) reformation c) recuperation d) health
2. plausible: a) planned b) believable c) debatable d) uncertain
3. foyer: a) hall b) fool c) envelop d) lobby
4. convalescent: a) sick b) recovering c) stupid d) misleading
5. plausibility: a) equivocation b) credibility c) rudeness d) pleading
6. convalesce: a) debilitate b) prevent c) recuperate d) divide

B. Supply the proper form of the most appropriate vocabulary word.

1. Even though Columbus believed the world was round, the idea did not seem ________________ to the rest of Europe.
2. Despite the accountant's considerable age, the doctor was hopeful that she would ________________ quickly after her heart attack.
3. John's ________________ smile and witty answer helped revive his sister's spirits.
4. There is little ________________ to José's story of finding fresh blueberries in that field during December.
5. The long, tedious period of ________________ following her injury bored the usually active athlete.

Lesson 15

cavalcade (n) (ˌkav-əl-ˈkād)

ORIGIN: Latin *caballus* (horse)
MEANING: A procession or sequence, often of persons riding on horseback or in vehicles
CONTEXT: "At the head of the *cavalcade* came the city officials, followed by members of every organization in the county."
SYNONYM: parade

integrate (v) (ˈint-ə-ˌgrāt)

ORIGIN: Latin *integrat* (made whole)
MEANING: To bring together or combine into a whole
CONTEXT: "Because the school had been *integrated* for years, students of different races and religions were good friends."
SYNONYMS: unify, desegregate, intermix, unite
ANTONYMS: segregate, separate
OTHER FORMS: integration (n.), integrative (adj.)

A. Circle the letter of the best meaning for each vocabulary word.

1. plausible: a) incredible b) separated c) reasonable d) laughable
2. convalescence: a) destruction b) relapse c) recovery d) operation
3. cavalcade: a) horse b) procession c) bugle call d) mounted soldier
4. integrate: a) desegregate b) separate c) ruin d) mystify
5. cavalcade: a) parade b) convalescence c) stroll d) walkway
6. integration: a) segregation b) unification c) supremacy d) ignorance

B. Supply the proper form of the most appropriate vocabulary word.

1. The ________________ of stars promised a spectacular evening of entertainment.
2. The ________________ of whether to accept the secure but dull secretarial job or to take the short-lived but glamorous offer in modeling threw Kristin into a quandary.
3. The ________________ of Steel Makers Limited and Iron Supplies Company into one corporation proved very profitable.
4. The ________________ of the doctor's diagnosis convinced the sick coal miner he should retire; it was indeed possible that long years of working in the mines had damaged his lungs.
5. The guards held back the jeering crowds as the ________________ of black limousines passed through the narrow street.

Lesson 16

Credence Relinquish

credence (n) (ˈkrēd-[ə]n[t]s)

ORIGIN: Latin *credent* (to believe) + *entia* (to be)
MEANING: Belief as to the truth of something
CONTEXT: "Because I have always found him to be truthful, I know I can give *credence* to his account of the accident."
SYNONYMS: credit, faith, trust, plausibility
ANTONYMS: disbelief, doubt
OTHER FORMS: credulity (n.), credibly (adv.), credible (adj.), incredible (adj.)

relinquish (v) (ri-ˈling-kwish)

ORIGIN: Latin *relinquir* (to leave behind)
MEANING: To give up, to abandon, to surrender
CONTEXT: "George *relinquished* all idea of running for president of the club and asked his supporters to vote for Tess."
SYNONYMS: yield, forego, cede, resign, abandon
ANTONYMS: keep, retain

A. Circle the letter of the best meaning for each vocabulary word.

1. credence: a) religion b) belief c) unification d) surrender
2. cavalcade: a) march tune b) procession c) militia d) flood
3. relinquish: a) stain b) hold fast c) update d) give up
4. credible: a) dissolvable b) worth cash c) uncertain d) believable
5. incredible: a) unbelievable b) valuable c) numerable d) small

B. Supply the proper form of the most appropriate vocabulary word.

1. Mr. Clement had to __________________ title to his car when he failed to make the payments to the loan company.
2. "I am unable to give any __________________ to your weak excuses," exclaimed the annoyed father when his daughter came home late without a good reason.
3. The two divisions of the company were more productive after they were __________________ under Harvey Davis.
4. Although I do not think the case for flying saucers is entirely __________________, I did see something last night that was very odd.
5. The ceremonial __________________ of mounted troops crowded the streets.
6. Mrs. Sanchez would not __________________ her hold over the family trust fund.

Lesson 17 *Using Word Parts to Unlock Meanings of Unfamiliar Words*

For persons who have spoken English all their lives, a word compounded from two English words, such as *flagpole*, presents no problem. Usually they already know the two English parts and can quickly derive the meaning of the new word.

A similar process can be used to determine the meanings of English words built on Greek and Latin parts. Since most native speakers of English are not automatically familiar with important Latin and Greek word parts, they have to learn them in order to unlock the meanings of unfamiliar English words built from these parts. Starting with this lesson, every fourth or fifth lesson will deal with important word parts borrowed from other languages — usually Greek or Latin. A knowledge of these word parts will give you the key to the meanings of thousands of English words.

But do not be swept away by the apparent effectiveness of this method. It will not work with every word built on a Latin or Greek root. For example, knowing that *de* is a Latin prefix meaning "down," "from," or "away," and that *testari* is a Latin root meaning "to call to witness" does not help very much in understanding the meaning of *detest* (to dislike intensely). Other clues, such as the context in which the word appears, must be taken into account if one is to use the word-analysis method for determining word meanings successfully.

Now here are the two word parts you are to learn for this lesson. Notice that for each, you are given the origin, the meaning or meanings, and a sample word in which this part appears. If the word part has variant spellings, these are given, along with sample words.

non- (prefix)

ORIGIN: Latin *non* (not)
MEANING: Not
CONTEXT: "*non*resident"

ex- (prefix)

ORIGIN: Latin *ex* (out)
MEANING: Out, away, from, beyond, former
CONTEXT: "*ex*hale"
OTHER FORMS: ef- (*ef*face), ec- (*ec*centric), es- (*es*cape), e- (*e*ducate)

A. In each of the italicized words below, underline the word part that you have learned. Then, using your knowledge of the meaning of the word part, circle the letter of the best meaning for the italicized word.

1. an unexpected *exodus*: a) arrival b) journey c) going away from d) increase
2. a *nonviolent* movement: a) doubtful b) trivial c) peaceful d) unimportant
3. *exotic* flowers: a) common b) purple c) out of the ordinary d) blooming

4. *exonerate* the man: a) enforce b) take away guilt c) put on d) increase

5. *nonsense* verse: a) rhythmic b) short c) romantic d) not sensible

6. question the *ex-convict:* a) one who fights for freedom b) one who is confined in prison c) former prisoner d) one who is about to be imprisoned

7. *export* the perfume: a) order b) bottle c) send quickly d) ship out of the country

8. *nonconductor* of electricity: a) one who invents uses of electricity b) machine that transmits electricity c) object that does not accept electrical current d) gauge that measures amount of electricity

9. *effusive* show of affection: a) unreal b) outpouring c) meager d) controlled

10. *nonessential* ingredients: a) removed b) not required c) baking d) important

11. *elapsed* period of time: a) constructively used b) wasted c) slipped away d) measured hourly

12. *estranged* husband: a) peculiar b) finicky c) separated from wife d) very angry

13. *nondescript* portrait: a) breathtakingly beautiful b) unclassifiable c) finished d) sketched

14. *nonpareil* leader: a) boastful b) unequaled c) spiritual d) deceptive

15. John's *ex-wife:* a) angry wife b) unhappy wife c) sweet wife d) former wife

B. REVIEW: Write one sentence for each of the following words. Each sentence must be complete enough to indicate the meaning of the vocabulary word through context clues and must not simply be an adaptation of a sentence in this book.

1. pert 2. rigor 3. convalescence 4. consummate 5. cavalcade
6. plausible 7. credence 8. gesticulate 9. integrate 10. relinquish

Lesson 18

Exotic Reek

exotic (adj) (ig-'zȧt-ik)

ORIGIN: Greek *exotikos* (foreign)
MEANING: Unusual or striking in effect or appearance; of foreign origin or character
CONTEXT: "You must see the *exotic* birds and flowers from the tropics; their coloring is very striking."
SYNONYMS: rare, bizarre, uncommon, alien
ANTONYMS: mundane, common, usual
OTHER FORMS: exoticness (n.), exotically (adv.)

reek (v) (rēk)

ORIGIN: Old English *rec* (smoke)
MEANING: To give off or become permeated with a strong, offensive odor
CONTEXT: "The air *reeked* with the smell of burning rubber."
SYNONYMS: stink, smell
ANTONYMS: perfume, scent, odorize
OTHER FORMS: reeking (adj.), reeky (adj.), reek (n.)

A. Circle the letter of the word in each group that does not belong.

1. a) belief b) credence c) trust d) convalescence
2. a) mundane b) ordinary c) common d) exotic
3. a) odor b) smell c) reek d) cavalcade
4. a) exotic b) rare c) bizarre d) mundane
5. a) convincing b) believable c) accredited d) equivocal

B. Supply the proper form of the most appropriate vocabulary word.

1. As the hot sun beat down on the marshy swamp, the stagnant water began to ________________.
2. Although the art dealer insisted the painting was a genuine Rembrandt, the museum refused to give ________________ to the painting's authenticity.
3. The kitchen ________________ with the smell of gas escaping from the faulty stove.
4. The couple enjoyed the ________________ sights, sounds, and smells of the Turkish Casbah.
5. If she wished to accept the post of federal judge, the wealthy investor had to ________________ her holdings in a profitable aerospace firm.

Lesson 19

exhilarate
intimation

intimation (n) (ˌint-ə-ˈmā-shən)

ORIGIN: Latin *intimat* (make known)
MEANING: A suggestion or a hint of something indirectly
CONTEXT: "His *intimation* that our neighbors were having financial trouble aroused our curiosity."
SYNONYMS: implication, indication, suggestion
ANTONYMS: declaration, announcement, assurance
OTHER FORM: intimate (v.)
NOTE: Do not confuse with *intimidation*, which means "the act of frightening."

exhilarate (v) (ig-ˈzil-ə-ˌrāt)

ORIGIN: Latin *exhilarat* (greatly gladdened)
MEANING: To make cheerful, to enliven, to invigorate
CONTEXT: "The cool, crisp mountain air *exhilarated* us."
SYNONYMS: cheer, elate, stimulate
ANTONYMS: depress, dull
OTHER FORMS: exhilaration (n.), exhilaratingly (adv.)

A. Circle the letter of the best meaning for each vocabulary word.

1. intimation: a) wink b) equivocation c) suggestion d) love affair
2. reek: a) smell b) scream c) cheat d) streak
3. convalescence: a) relapse b) weakening c) recovery d) delay
4. exhilarate: a) speed b) drill c) uncover d) stimulate
5. intimate: a) hint b) gossip c) prevent d) insulate

B. Supply the proper form of the most appropriate vocabulary word.

1. Although Daisy knew Bill was going to win the prize, she gave no ________________ of her knowledge, greeting him with a smile that implied nothing.
2. The ________________ jog in the fresh morning air cheered the woman.
3. Even though they are not ________________, the daisies and heather that grow behind the shed are Ramon's favorite flowers.
4. At the first ________________ of a storm, the outdoor theater canceled its evening show.
5. The race across the wet sand dunes ________________ the children, livening their spirits after the heavy rain.
6. Although the diplomat's speech did not openly express disapproval, the look on his face ________________ his displeasure.

Lesson 20

slovenly (adj) (ˈsləv-ən-lē)

ORIGIN: Middle English *sloveyn* (rascal)
MEANING: Habitually unclean and untidy
CONTEXT: "The *slovenly* old man invited us into a cabin that was as dirty and untidy as he."
SYNONYMS: careless, unkempt, slatternly, uncultivated
ANTONYMS: neat, clean, fastidious
OTHER FORM: slovenliness (n.)

voluminous (adj) (və-ˈlü-mə-nəs)

ORIGIN: Late Latin *voluminos* (full of folds)
MEANING: Of great size, volume, or extent
CONTEXT: "The *voluminous* notes she took during the lectures on China filled several notebooks."
SYNONYMS: abundant, comprehensive, ample
ANTONYMS: slight, limited
OTHER FORMS: voluminously (adv.), voluminousness (n.)

A. Circle the letter of the best meaning for each vocabulary word.

1. slovenly: a) fastidious b) slight c) unkempt d) elderly
2. gesticulate: a) digest b) graduate c) gesture d) doubt
3. exhilarate: a) accelerate b) decrease c) enliven d) cut out
4. voluminous: a) evaporated b) spirited c) ample d) slatternly
5. voluminousness: a) limitation b) abundance c) pleats d) strength
6. slovenliness: a) fastidiousness b) carelessness c) equivocation d) heaviness

B. Supply the proper form of the most appropriate vocabulary word.

1. We bought a(n) ____________________ amount of material in order to make the ornate nineteenth-century costumes for *She Stoops to Conquer*.
2. The rebellious young student's ____________________ appearance was just one indication that he wanted no part of a nine-to-five job.
3. Although the boss ____________________ that the plant might close early the day before Christmas, she would make no definite promise.
4. The ____________________ amount of paperwork that had to be finished each day kept the overworked city employees at their desks long after the normal quitting time.
5. The toothpaste advertised on television was reputed to have a fresh ____________________ flavor.

Lesson 21

RAMPANT EXUBERANCE

exuberance (n) (ig-ˈzü-b[ə]-rən[t]s)

ORIGIN: Latin *exuberare* (to be abundant)
MEANING: High spirits; joyously unrestrained enthusiasm
CONTEXT: "The children, expressing their *exuberance* by running through the woods, soon tired their grandfather, who was looking after them."
SYNONYMS: elation, exhilaration
ANTONYM: listlessness
OTHER FORMS: exuberant (adj.), exuberantly (adv.)

rampant (adj) (ˈram-pənt)

ORIGIN: Old French *ramper* (to ramp)
MEANING: Prevalent; violent in action or spirit; raging
CONTEXT: "Rumors about who will be the new Supreme Court justice are running *rampant* throughout Washington, D.C."
SYNONYMS: unbridled, widespread, turbulent
ANTONYMS: moderate, controlled, limited

A. Circle the letter of the best meaning for each vocabulary word.

1. rampant: a) pertaining to ramparts b) jogging c) turbulent d) controlled
2. exuberance: a) suspicion b) gesticulation c) elation d) moderation
3. exuberant: a) prevalent b) enthusiastic c) sad d) mistaken
4. slovenly: a) enslaved b) tired c) untidy d) fastidious
5. rampant: a) slippery b) supported c) widespread d) sorry
6. cavalcade: a) wharf b) soldier c) procession d) surmise

B. Supply the proper form of the most appropriate vocabulary word.

1. Completing the final report on the proposed missile system required ________________ amounts of special typing paper.
2. In the enclosed towns of medieval Europe, a(n) ________________ epidemic could quickly kill an entire populace.
3. When the armed forces returned from Europe and from the Pacific after World War II, the American public was ________________.
4. Having received an A on her English paper, Sharon was ________________.
5. Discontent among the ranks ran ________________ when the sergeant unjustly punished a private.

Lesson 22

com
junct

com- (prefix)

ORIGIN: Latin *cum* (with, together)
MEANING: With, together
CONTEXT: "*com*press"
OTHER FORMS: col- (*col*laborate), co- (*co*education), con- (*con*vocation)

-junct- (root)

ORIGIN: Latin *jungere* (to join)
MEANING: To join
CONTEXT: "*junct*ion"
OTHER FORM: -jug- (con*jug*ate)

A. In each of the italicized words below, underline the word parts that you have learned. Then, using your knowledge of the meanings of the word parts, circle the letter of the best meaning for the italicized word. (For some words there may be only one word part.)

1. *compressing* machine: a) cleaning b) separating c) squeezing d) digging
2. *conjunction* in the sentence: a) punctuation b) describing word c) joining word d) subject
3. jury *concurred:* a) disputed b) discussed c) agreed with one another d) argued
4. *cooperative* enterprise: a) easy b) enjoyable c) forward looking d) acting together
5. *nonparticipant* member: a) leading b) uninvolved c) quarrelsome d) elected
6. *concomitant* joy: a) parental b) brief c) spiritual d) occurring with something else
7. *exempt* from taxation: a) decreased rate of taxation b) out of the realm of taxation c) legality of taxation d) rigorous collection of taxes
8. *juncture* of bones: a) cells b) joint c) fracture d) skeleton
9. *disjunctive* action: a) criminal b) separating c) intelligent d) genuine

B. REVIEW: Write one sentence for each of the following words. Each sentence must be complete enough to indicate the meaning of the vocabulary word through context clues and must not simply be an adaptation of a sentence in this book.

1. slovenly 2. rampant 3. intimation 4. voluminous 5. reek
6. exotic 7. exuberance 8. exhilarate 9. surmise 10. dilemma

Lesson 23

concerted (adj) (kən-ˈsərt-əd)

ORIGIN: Latin *com* (with) + *certare* (to strive)
MEANING: Planned, devised, or performed together
CONTEXT: "The civic organizations of our city made a *concerted* effort to provide food for the needy at Christmas."
SYNONYMS: determined, agreed, harmonious
ANTONYMS: unorganized, discordant
OTHER FORMS: concertedly (adv.), concert (n. or v.)

tawny (adj) (ˈtȯ-nē)

ORIGIN: Middle French *taner* (to tan)
MEANING: Of a dark yellowish or dull yellowish-brown color
CONTEXT: "The lioness, a huge *tawny* beast, paced the iron cage."
SYNONYMS: dusky, tan
OTHER FORM: tawniness (n.)

A. Circle the letter of the best meaning for each vocabulary word.

1. tawny: a) slovenly b) tawdry c) tan d) stretched
2. concerted: a) agreed b) yellowish c) doubtful d) shortened
3. rampant: a) wet b) controlled c) raging d) unified
4. tawny: a) rising b) glistening c) dusky d) definite
5. exuberant: a) enthusiastic b) questioned c) decreased d) deflated
6. concerted: a) equivocal b) determined c) sloppy d) excited

B. Supply the proper form of the most appropriate vocabulary word.

1. The ____________ efforts of the sanitation department and the public resulted in considerably cleaner streets.
2. When the lacrosse coach invited Wendy to join the team, she was ____________.
3. Jan's kitten was a yellowish-brown, or ____________ -colored, Persian with black markings on its face and paws.
4. The old couple rocked peacefully on their front porch, happily reminiscing about their *(nuptial)* ____________ life.
5. Despite the ____________ efforts of the fund-raising committee, the church failed to collect enough money to build the new addition.

Lesson 24

PERVERSE · CONTEXT

perverse (adj) (ˌpər-ˈvərs)

ORIGIN: Latin *perversus* (askew)
MEANING: Being determined to oppose what is expected or desired
CONTEXT: "That child is surely in a *perverse* mood today; every time I tell her to do one thing she does another."
SYNONYMS: stubborn, headstrong, contrary
ANTONYMS: agreeable, tractable, normal, manageable
OTHER FORM: perversity (n.)

context (n) (ˈkän-ˌtekst)

ORIGIN: Latin *contextus* (a joining together)
MEANING: An overall environment that helps to interpret a particular aspect of that environment
CONTEXT: "Studying a word in its *context* generally will reveal its meaning, at least in part."
SYNONYMS: milieu, environment, surroundings
OTHER FORM: contextual (adj.)

A. Circle the letter of the best meaning for each vocabulary word.

1. context: a) stubbornness b) environment c) contentment d) love
2. perverse: a) dirty b) headstrong c) doubtful d) bookish
3. exuberance: a) frustration b) elation c) acceleration d) exit
4. perversity: a) portion b) old age c) stubbornness d) mystery
5. concerted: a) flowery b) tolerated c) determined d) unconducted
6. tawny: a) tawdry b) torn c) weak d) tan

B. Supply the proper form of the most appropriate vocabulary word.

1. "The ________________ of the entire book may shed some light on those rather difficult passages in Chapter 3," instructed the lecturer.
2. Although Cora's brothers and sisters are all obedient and cooperative, Cora is truly ________________!
3. Through the ________________ efforts of their friends, the family was able to escape the tyranny of the secret police.
4. The ________________ of the scientist in clinging to her disproved theory was a mystery to her colleagues.
5. You should not quote people out of ________________ for fear of misrepresenting their ideas.

Lesson 25

lax (adj) (laks)

ORIGIN: Latin *lax* (loose, slack)
MEANING: Lacking in strictness; careless, negligent
CONTEXT: "Because the discipline of many beginning teachers is *lax*, their classes get out of control."
SYNONYMS: easy, loose, slack, flexible, neglectful, indolent
ANTONYMS: rigid, strict, rigorous
OTHER FORMS: laxly (adv.), laxness (n.)

gloat (v) (glōt)

ORIGIN: Scandinavian *glotta* (to grin scornfully)
MEANING: To look at or think about with great satisfaction
CONTEXT: "She *gloated* over her daughter's achievement until all her friends were disgusted."
SYNONYMS: exult, crow, delight in, glory
ANTONYMS: ignore, mourn, regret, grieve

A. Circle the letter of the word that best completes each analogy.

1. improper: proper : : _______: agreeable
   a) gloating b) equivocal c) perverse d) exuberant
2. looseness: strictness : : _______: rigor
   a) laxness b) fastidiousness c) credulity d) intimation
3. forest: tree : : _______: passage
   a) austerity b) context c) equivocation d) perversity
4. exult: grieve : : _______: regret
   a) accelerate b) lament c) gesticulate d) gloat

B. Supply the proper form of the most appropriate vocabulary word.

1. When we were disqualified from the race, our competitors ________________ for days.
2. The ________________ efforts of volunteer workers throughout the community helped the United Fund campaign surpass its goal.
3. The company's ________________ in enforcing the safety regulations at the plant resulted in a disastrous accident.
4. The careless student received a warning from the principal regarding her ________________ attendance record.

-cap- (root)

ORIGIN: Latin *capere* (to take, to seize)
MEANING: To take
CONTEXT: "*cap*ture"
OTHER FORMS: -cep- (de*cep*tion), -cept- (inter*cept*), -cip- (in*cip*ient)

-flu- (root)

ORIGIN: Latin *fluere* (to flow, to wave)
MEANING: To flow
CONTEXT: "*flu*ent"
OTHER FORMS: -flux- (in*flux*), -fluous- (super*fluous*)

A. In each of the italicized words below, circle the word parts that you have learned. Then, using your knowledge of the meanings of the word parts, circle the letter of the best meaning for the italicized word. (For some words there may be only one word part.)

1. *accept* the reprimand: a) reject b) forbid c) ignore d) take
2. the fugitive's *captor:* a) plan b) route c) arrester d) escape
3. *confluence* of ideas: a) scattering b) flowing together c) testing d) birth
4. *reception* of wedding guests: a) excitement b) movement c) welcoming d) number
5. *fluctuating* stock market: a) reliable b) steady c) moving up and down d) quiet
6. held *captive:* a) held prisoner b) held loosely c) held over d) held up
7. *fluent* French: a) mispronounced b) archaic c) colloquial d) flowing
8. tissue that is *nonviable:* a) cancerous b) continuous c) taken apart d) not capable of growth
9. *effluence* of the tributary: a) outflowing b) riverbeds c) drying up d) richness
10. *junction* of two roads: a) construction b) repair c) danger d) coming together

B. REVIEW: Write one sentence for each of the following words. Each sentence must be complete enough to indicate the meaning of the vocabulary word through context clues and must not simply be an adaptation of a sentence in this book.

1. perverse 2. lax 3. integrate 4. context 5. gloat
6. concerted 7. plausible 8. pert 9. credence 10. consummate

Lesson 27

diverse (adj) (dī-ˈvərs)

ORIGIN: Latin *divers* (to divert)
MEANING: Of a different kind, form, or character
CONTEXT: "He and his brother are of very *diverse* natures."
SYNONYMS: dissimilar, unlike, varied, manifold
ANTONYMS: similar, singular
OTHER FORMS: diversity (n.), diversification (n.), diversely (adv.), diversified (adj.), divers (adj.)

belittle (v) (bi-ˈlit-l)

ORIGIN: Old English *bi* (near) + *lytil* (small)
MEANING: To make something seem less important
CONTEXT: "I think Bill *belittles* the success of others because he is jealous."
SYNONYMS: minimize, depreciate, disparage, decry, deprecate
ANTONYMS: inflate, praise
OTHER FORMS: belittlement (n.), belittler (n.)

A. Circle the letter of the best meaning for each vocabulary word.

1. belittle: a) inflate b) vary c) deprecate d) divert
2. bungler: a) bugler b) dreamer c) joker d) mishandler
3. rampant: a) single b) weakened c) gleeful d) widespread
4. diverse: a) polite b) stubborn c) perverse d) varied
5. belittle: a) equivocate b) surmise c) chalk up d) minimize

B. Supply the proper form of the most appropriate vocabulary word.

1. Because Ruth's interests are so ________________, she is a member of many different clubs.
2. "Don't continually ________________ my work," retorted the playwright, who was weary of uninformed criticism.
3. To prepare college students for many different types of careers, the university offers a(n) ________________ curriculum.
4. Since there was such ________________ of opinion, the student council could not agree on a policy.
5. Stubbornly clinging to her decision, the ________________ child obstinately refused to come out of the pool.

Lesson 28

urban (adj) (ˈər-ban)

ORIGIN: Latin *urb* (city)
MEANING: Pertaining to a city or town
CONTEXT: "Although I prefer living in the country, most of my family enjoy *urban* life."
SYNONYMS: civic, metropolitan, municipal
ANTONYMS: country, rural, rustic
OTHER FORMS: urbanize (v.), urbanite (n.), urbanization (n.)

urbane (adj) (ər-ˈbān)

ORIGIN: Latin *urbanus* (city)
MEANING: Having the polish regarded as characteristic of sophisticated social life found in major cities
CONTEXT: "At the reunion, Helen's *urbane* manner contrasted sharply with that of her friends from smaller towns."
SYNONYMS: suave, cultivated, sophisticated
ANTONYMS: simple, countrified

A. Circle the letter of the best meaning for each vocabulary word.

1. urban: a) sophisticated b) outlying c) municipal d) busy
2. urbane: a) foolish b) civic c) sophisticated d) central
3. belittle: a) depreciate b) adore c) convince d) waver
4. diverse: a) varied b) united c) stubborn d) fastidious
5. urbanite: a) apartment dweller b) world traveler c) innkeeper d) city dweller

B. Supply the proper form of the most appropriate vocabulary word.

1. Mark's ________________ manner distinguished him immediately from the rustic farmers with whom he was dealing.
2. ________________ redevelopment programs provide better facilities for city residents.
3. The ________________ of the family's problems astounded the social worker, who had never encountered so many different problems on one case.
4. The jealous brother ________________ the achievements of his older sister in order to make himself look better.
5. The ________________ jeweller's good manners and fashionable clothes reassured the wealthy customers.

Lesson 29

BUTTRESS POSTULATE

buttress (n) ('bə-trəs)

ORIGIN: Old French *baterez* (abutment)
MEANING: A prop or support
CONTEXT: "The PTA's unanimous endorsement of Ms. French was a *buttress* to her when she sought election to the board."
SYNONYMS: brace, reinforcement, bolster
OTHER FORM: buttress (v.)

postulate (n) ('päs-chə-,lət)

ORIGIN: Latin *postulatum* (thing requested)
MEANING: Something taken as self-evident or assumed without proof as a basis for reasoning
CONTEXT: "The geometry class did not have to prove the *postulate* because it was considered a self-evident property of the triangle."
SYNONYMS: theory, axiom, assumption
OTHER FORMS: postulation (n.), postulate (v.)

A. Match each vocabulary word with its synonym by writing the proper letter in the blank.

1. urbane ______ 2. postulate ______ 3. rampant ______
4. buttress (n.) ______ 5. urban ______ 6. buttress (v.) ______

a) support b) raging c) reinforce d) civic e) sophisticated f) assumption

B. Supply the proper form of the most appropriate vocabulary word.

1. The ________________ in the Gothic church was so beautifully carved that most tourists viewed it as mere decoration, rarely guessing it served as a support.
2. The ________________ in the scientific theory did not require proof.
3. On summer weekends, people from ________________ centers flock to resort areas, trying to escape the heat and congestion of the cities.
4. The socialite's ________________ manner fascinated the unsophisticated girl.
5. The biologist's new theory ________________ the existence of DNA.
6. The workers ________________ the sagging wharf with several new pilings.
7. The note of *(uncertainty)* ________________ in the physician's voice puzzled the patient who did not understand why the doctor was being ambiguous.

Lesson 30

CONGLOMERATE URCHIN

urchin (n) ('ər-chən)

ORIGIN: Latin *horrere* (to bristle or tremble)
MEANING: A pert or roguish youngster
CONTEXT: "Having snatched a couple of apples from the tree, the *urchin* ran down the road laughing gleefully."
SYNONYMS: waif, ragamuffin

conglomerate (adj) (kən-'glȧm-[ə]rət)

ORIGIN: Latin *conglomeratus* (to roll together)
MEANING: Made up of parts from various sources or of various kinds
CONTEXT: "Dad took a *conglomerate* handful of articles from Dave's pocket before he washed Dave's jeans."
SYNONYM: accumulated
OTHER FORMS: conglomeration (n.), conglomerate (n. or v.)

A. Circle the letter of the best meaning for each vocabulary word.

1. buttress: a) inflate b) brace c) deceive d) fight
2. urchin: a) seashell b) waif c) insult d) jerky movement
3. conglomerate: a) varied b) sticky c) glued d) troublesome
4. postulate: a) letter b) weight c) pendulum d) theory
5. urchin: a) urn b) tropical plant c) tree d) ragamuffin
6. conglomerate: a) wadded b) accumulated c) dusky d) polite

B. Supply the proper form of the most appropriate vocabulary word.

1. His polished accent and walking cane gave the elderly editor a very ________________ air.
2. A(n) ________________ group of applicants appeared in the casting office when the studio announced an audition for "extras" for the new cowboy film.
3. The mathematical ________________ was used in the formulation of the theory.
4. The fastidious mother thought her son's friends were a rowdy gang of ________________.
5. The sarcastic reply of the ragged ________________ offended the social worker.
6. Ditman Industries, a(n) ________________ composed of many wholly owned subsidiaries, has just announced the purchase of two new companies.

-pon- (root)

ORIGIN: Latin *ponere* (to put)
MEANING: To place, put
CONTEXT: "op*pon*ent"
OTHER FORMS: -pose- (im*pose*), -posit- (de*posit*), -pos- (com*pos*ure)

-ject- (root)

ORIGIN: Latin *jacere* (to throw)
MEANING: To throw
CONTEXT: "e*ject*"
OTHER FORM: -jac- (e*jac*ulate)

A. In each of the italicized words below, underline the word parts that you have learned. Then, using your knowledge of the meanings of the word parts, circle the letter of the best meaning for the italicized word. (For some words there may be only one word part.)

1. *propose* change: a) throw away b) put forward c) uphold d) weaken
2. *eject* the missile: a) throw out b) destroy c) build d) design
3. *object* to the policy: a) throw up a challenge b) approve c) form d) unify
4. *reposit* gold: a) spend b) exchange c) replace d) mine
5. *capacity* of the tank: a) lining b) level c) amount held d) source
6. *position* of the furniture: a) care b) strength c) luster d) place
7. rocket *trajectory:* a) orbit it has been thrown into b) exhaust that forms a vapor trail c) landing area d) design by an expert
8. *superfluous* glue: a) sticky b) excessive c) bottled d) expensive
9. *project* the budget: a) exceed b) amend c) extend ahead d) approve
10. *deposit* the mail: a) post b) cancel c) weigh d) put down

B. REVIEW: Write one sentence for each of the following words. Each sentence must be complete enough to indicate the meaning of the vocabulary word through context clues and must not be simply an adaptation of a sentence in this book.

1. diverse 2. gloat 3. postulate 4. urbane 5. belittle
6. voluminous 7. urchin 8. relinquish 9. buttress (n.) 10. urban

Lesson 32

residue (n) (ʹrez-ə-d[y]ü)

ORIGIN: Latin *residum* (what is left over)
MEANING: That which remains after a part is taken, gone, or disposed of
CONTEXT: "The *residue* left in the urn after the coffee is poured is the grounds."
SYNONYMS: remainder, remnant, dregs
OTHER FORMS: residual (adj. or n.), residually (adv.)

embark (v) (im-ʹbȧrk)

ORIGIN: Middle French *embarcar* (bark)
MEANING: To venture or to invest in an enterprise or activity; often, to board a ship
CONTEXT: "I feel that Juan is a little old to *embark* on a career that will require two additional years of college."
SYNONYMS: begin, commence, board
ANTONYM: disembark
OTHER FORM: embarkation (n.)

A. Circle the letter of the best meaning of each vocabulary word.

1. embark: a) sharpen b) strip c) begin d) run
2. residue: a) resident b) resolution c) remains d) retreat
3. urchin: a) jerk b) ragamuffin c) deception d) connection
4. residual: a) remainder b) reception c) transient d) resident
5. martial: a) married b) confused c) bellicose d) glorified

B. Supply the proper form of the most appropriate vocabulary word.

1. The white poodle belonging to the *(meticulous)* ________________ Mr. Kessel was closely sheared and perfectly groomed.
2. "Passengers departing aboard Flight 907 will ________________ from Gate 3," droned the voice over the loudspeaker in the terminal.
3. The milk souring on the porch ________________ so strongly it nauseated the visitor.
4. The ________________ left in the bottom of wine bottles is the dregs.
5. The ________________ of the troops required a fleet of transport ships.
6. Nowadays, the ________________ from processing paper is recycled for profit.

propriety (n) (p[r]ə-ˈprī-ət-ē)

ORIGIN: Latin *proprius* (one's own)
MEANING: Conformity to established standards of proper behavior or manners
CONTEXT: "The *propriety* of their behavior can always be depended upon to be perfect for the occasion."
SYNONYMS: etiquette, correctness, fitness, decency, decorum, protocol
ANTONYMS: perversity, ineptitude, impropriety

endorse (v) (in-ˈdȯ[ə]rs)

ORIGIN: Middle Latin *endorore* (to put on the back)
MEANING: To approve, support, or sustain
CONTEXT: "If Ms. Ambrose is *endorsed* by the labor unions, she will have a better chance of being elected."
SYNONYMS: sanction, uphold, back, second, ratify, confirm
ANTONYMS: disapprove, oppose
OTHER FORMS: endorser (n.), endorsable (adj.), endorsement (n.)

A. Circle the letter of the word that best completes each analogy.

1. finickiness: fastidiousness : : _______: sanction

   a) tidiness b) embarkation c) endorsement d) slovenliness

2. gloating: regretful : : _______: perverse

   a) exultant b) stubborn c) proper d) delayed

3. bungle: mistake : : _______: remains

   a) blunder b) beginning c) residue d) buttress

B. Supply the proper form of the most appropriate vocabulary word.

1. Eva Johnson _______________ the check so that the teller would know she wanted it cashed.
2. "Before we _______________ on our expedition, let's check the gear," suggested Ed.
3. The _______________ of Mr. Hollbrook by the influential civil rights leaders ensured his election as mayor.
4. When the assistant barged into the conference room without knocking, the boss, engrossed in an important discussion, angrily fired him for lack of _______________.
5. After the series of chemistry experiments were done, we threw away the _______________ left in the bottom of the flask.

Lesson 34

edifice (n) ('ed-ə-fəs)

ORIGIN: Latin *aedificium* (building)
MEANING: A building of imposing appearance or large size
CONTEXT: "The modern architect designed an *edifice* constructed of glass and steel."
SYNONYM: structure
OTHER FORM: edify (v.)

edify (v) ('ed-ə-ˌfī)

ORIGIN: Latin *aedificare* (to build)
MEANING: To build up or increase the faith or morality of; to uplift
CONTEXT: "There are many secular as well as religious paintings that *edify* the viewer."
SYNONYMS: enlighten, educate, benefit, illumine
ANTONYMS: darken, perplex, confuse
OTHER FORMS: edifying (adj.), edification (n.)

A. Circle the letter of the best meaning for each vocabulary word.

1. edifice: a) face b) enlightenment c) strucure d) design
2. endorse: a) adore b) approve c) bury d) plant
3. propriety: a) ownership b) silence c) education d) correctness
4. edification: a) imagination b) enlightenment c) prayer d) deception
5. postulate: a) wear out b) theorize c) excavate d) escape

B. Supply the proper form of the most appropriate vocabulary word.

1. Mother insisted we attend the revival meeting since she believed that the evangelist would be ____________.
2. Deeply interested in architectural design, Christopher took forty photographs of the unusually old ____________.
3. The highly informative and stimulating lecture on the role of the federal government in state affairs was ____________.
4. The ____________ was gutted by a spectacular fire when the blitzkrieg hit downtown London.
5. Because ____________ was expected at the diplomatic reception, we decided to wear formal evening attire.

Lesson 35

condolence (n) (kən-'dō-lən[t]s)

ORIGIN: Latin *condole* (to feel pain) + *entia* (state)
MEANING: Expression of sympathy with another in sorrow, grief, or misfortune
CONTEXT: "It is considered good manners to write a note of *condolence* to a friend in time of sorrow."
SYNONYMS: solace, sympathy
ANTONYM: pitilessness

paraphernalia (n) (par-ə-fə[r]-'nāl-yə)

ORIGIN: Greek *parapherna* (goods a bride brings over and above the dowry)
MEANING: Personal belongings; equipment
CONTEXT: "The fishing *paraphernalia* filled the boat."
SYNONYMS: gear, effects, trappings

A. Circle the letter of the best meaning for each vocabulary word.

1. paraphernalia: a) paratrooper b) suitcase c) belongings d) emotions
2. edify: a) eat quickly b) solve c) join d) enlighten
3. condolence: a) congratulations b) pitilessness c) condoning d) solace
4. endorse: a) confuse b) cajole c) support d) adore
5. convalescence: a) sympathy b) debilitation c) recuperation d) turnover

B. Supply the proper form of the most appropriate vocabulary word.

1. The astonished mother stared at all the ________________ her children had planned to take on a one-week vacation.
2. The panel discussion on the role of art in society was ________________.
3. When Marie was killed, Joe sent a letter of ________________ to her brother.
4. The old ________________ lent an element of charm to the narrow street where most of the other nineteenth-century buildings had been torn down.
5. Ann O'Riley was unaware of the ________________ she had collected over the years until she began rummaging around the cluttered attic.
6. Even though Rita did not know Mr. Hamilton well, she wanted to express her ________________ over his wife's death.

-log- (root)

ORIGIN: Greek *logos* (speech, word)
MEANING: Word, thought, speech, discourse, reason, study of
CONTEXT: "*log*ic"
OTHER FORMS: -logo- (*logo*gram), -logue- (mono*logue*), -logy- (psycho*logy*)

-cogn- (root)

ORIGIN: Latin *cognoscere* (to know)
MEANING: To know
CONTEXT: "re*cogn*ize"
OTHER FORM: -cog- (*cog*itation)

A. In each of the italicized words below, underline the word part that you have learned. Then, using your knowledge of the meanings of the word parts, circle the letter of the best meaning of the italicized word.

1. *cognition* tests: a) hearing b) speech c) knowledge d) continuity
2. *anthology* of poetry: a) rhythms b) collected writings c) knowledge d) death
3. *anticipate* trouble: a) take precautions for b) hasten c) search for d) find
4. *recognizable* trait: a) reasonable b) hidden c) observable d) pitiable
5. infallible *logic:* a) thought process b) machine c) flow d) person
6. *cognoscente* of wines: a) seller b) person who has knowledge c) ignorance d) dislike
7. *eulogy* at the graveside: a) crowd b) mourner c) speech d) silence
8. *cognizant* of differences: a) full b) knowledgeable c) devoid d) ignorant
9. preparation in *theology:* a) theater design b) study of religion c) salesmanship d) scientific knowledge

B. REVIEW: Write one sentence for each of the following words. Each sentence must be complete enough to indicate the meaning of the vocabulary word through context clues and must not simply be an adaptation of a sentence in this book.

1. paraphernalia 2. condolence 3. residue 4. edifice 5. embark
6. urchin 7. edify 8. vagrant 9. endorse 10. conglomerate (adj.)

Lesson 37

connive (v) (kə-'nīv)

ORIGIN: Latin *conivere* (to close the eyes)
MEANING: To cooperate secretly or have a secret understanding
CONTEXT: "The head of that company *connived* with the mayor to get the contract for paving the city streets."
SYNONYMS: conspire, intrigue, deceive, scheme, plot
OTHER FORMS: conniver (n.), connivingly (adv.), connivance (n.)

theology (n) (thē-'äl-ə-jē)

ORIGIN: Greek *the* (God) + *logia* (word)
MEANING: The study and interpretation of religious faith, practice, and experience
CONTEXT: "Since he plans to become a minister, he will enter a school of *theology* after graduating from college."
OTHER FORMS: theological (adj.), theologue (n.), theologian (n.)

A. Circle the letter of the best meaning for each vocabulary word.

1. theology: a) logic b) speech c) religion d) education
2. connive: a) conspire b) console c) confuse d) condole
3. embark: a) shout b) decrease c) commence d) perfect
4. theological: a) religious b) perfect c) pious d) aesthetic
5. buttress: a) inflation b) weakness c) force d) support

B. Supply the proper form of the most appropriate vocabulary word.

1. The conspirators ____________________ to overthrow the government.
2. Larry's college course in ____________________ helped him to understand his own religious beliefs.
3. Although rumors of peace were rampant, the soldiers did not think they were *(credible)* ____________________.
4. After distilling the water to rid it of unwanted minerals, a whitish ____________________ was left inside the bottle.
5. The ____________________ visited the college to give a lecture on the many kinds of religion practiced in the United States.
6. Grandma discovered the *(ragamuffins)* ____________________ hiding under the barn.

Lesson 38

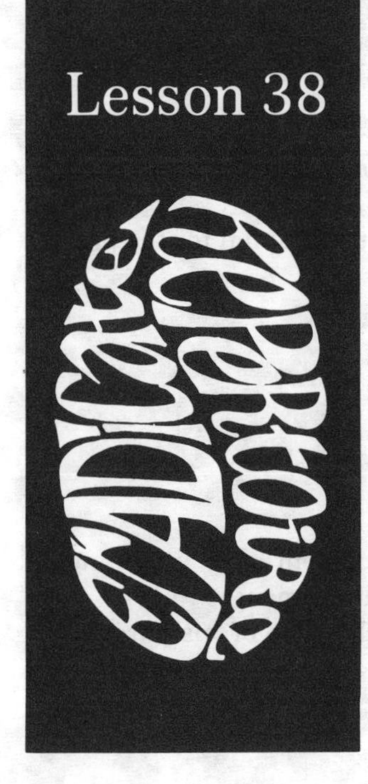

repertoire (n) ('rep-ə[r]-,twär)

ORIGIN: Late Latin *repertor* (catalog, inventory)
MEANING: A list that a company or person is prepared to perform
CONTEXT: "The singer has a large *repertoire* of music from which she can draw for a performance."
OTHER FORM: repertory (n. or adj.)

eradicate (v) (i-'rad-ə-,kāt)

ORIGIN: Late Latin *eradicat* (rooted out)
MEANING: To remove, destroy, pull up, do away with completely
CONTEXT: "The treaty *eradicated* the threat of nuclear destruction and restored mutual trust among nations."
SYNONYMS: obliterate, erase, exterminate, annihilate
ANTONYMS: add, create, establish
OTHER FORMS: eradication (n.), eradicative (adj.), eradicator (n.)

A. Circle the letter of the best meaning for each vocabulary word.

1. connive: a) contend b) punish c) reprieve d) scheme
2. eradication: a) make-believe b) radiation c) elimination d) raise
3. repertoire: a) pertness b) retort c) reprieve d) things that can be performed
4. connive: a) decrease b) surmise c) plot d) scrutinize
5. eradicator: a) radiator b) trick c) eraser d) establishment
6. theologian: a) cook b) minister c) doctor d) seamstress

B. Supply the proper form of the most appropriate vocabulary word.

1. The cleaning solution could not ________________ the child's greasy fingerprints from the newly hung wallpaper.
2. The vaudeville troupe had an extensive ________________ of pantomime, dancing, and humorous songs.
3. The ________________ theater, experimenting with a wide variety of new plays, offered several different productions a week during the summer months.
4. Jewish ________________ is based on a belief in the existence of one God.
5. Outlaws would ________________ their footprints by dragging a branch behind them.
6. The rebels ________________ with the military to overthrow the unpopular government.

stupor (n) ('st[y]ü-pər)

ORIGIN: Latin *stup* (senseless) + *or* (state)
MEANING: A condition in which sense or feeling is greatly diminished or suspended
CONTEXT: "She has been lying in a *stupor* in the hospital for the past two days."
SYNONYMS: lethargy, apathy, torpor, languor
ANTONYMS: alertness, animation
OTHER FORMS: stuporous (adj.), stupefy (v.)

nurture (v) ('nər-chər)

ORIGIN: Latin *nutritura* (a nourishing)
MEANING: To promote the growth and development of by providing necessary food, support, and encouragement
CONTEXT: "Dan's aunt *nurtured* him from the time of his parents' death until he finished college."
SYNONYMS: rear, foster, sustain, nourish, educate
ANTONYMS: deprive, neglect
OTHER FORM: nurturance (n.)

A. Circle the letter of the word that best completes each analogy.

1. dullness: exuberance : : ______: animation
   a) exhilaration b) alertness c) stupor d) stupidity
2. gesticulate: gesture : : ______: foster
   a) motion b) bungle c) nurture d) stupefy
3. integrated: unified : : ______: apathetic
   a) stuporous b) destructive c) kind d) alert
4. stupor: torpor : : ______: nourishment
   a) lethargy b) fasting c) clothing d) nurturance

B. Supply the proper form of the most appropriate vocabulary word.

1. We carefully ______________ the exotic flowering plants in the greenhouse.
2. When the sedative took effect, the old man fell into a(n)______________.
3. Jean lay in a(n) ______________, lethargically sunning herself on the white, glistening sand.
4. "If you do make a mistake,______________ it with the special eraser given you," she instructed.
5. The ______________ of the talented pianist was diverse and well-chosen.

Lesson 40

intra- (prefix)

ORIGIN: Latin *intra* (within)
MEANING: Within, during
CONTEXT: "*intra*state"
OTHER FORM: intro- (*intro*vert)
NOTE: Do not confuse *intra-* with *inter-*, which means "between" or "among."

hyper- (prefix)

ORIGIN: Greek *hyper* (more, over)
MEANING: Excessive, more than enough
CONTEXT: "*hyper*critical"
NOTE: Do not confuse *hyper-* with *hydro-*, which means "water" as in *hydro*electric, or with *hypo-*, which means "beneath," "less," or "lower," as in *hypo*dermic.

A. In each of the italicized words below, underline the word parts that you have learned. Then, using your knowledge of the meanings of the word parts, circle the letter of the best meaning for the italicized word. (For some words there may be only one word part.)

1. people *intermingled:* a) connived b) scattered with confusion c) took cover d) moved among one another
2. *intramural* sports: a) sports organized between states b) sports organized among nations c) sports organized along the seaboard d) sports organized within one school
3. *hypersensitivity* to penicillin: a) having no reaction b) having a weak reaction c) having a small reaction d) having an excessive reaction
4. *interscholastic* competition: a) competition between schools b) competition within a school c) competition outside of school d) competition during school
5. *introspective* woman: a) one who specializes in skin diseases b) one who looks within herself c) one who travels between cities d) one who makes friends easily
6. *intercept* the message: a) send b) interpret c) seize in transit d) write

B. REVIEW: Write one sentence for each of the following words. Each sentence must be complete enough to indicate the meaning of the vocabulary word through context clues and must not simply be an adaptation of a sentence in this book.

1. nurture 2. theology 3. stupor 4. aesthetic 5. marital
6. connive 7. eradicate 8. foyer 9. repertoire 10. propriety

Lesson 41

hypothesis (n) (hī-ˈpäth-ə-səs)

ORIGIN: Greek *hypothesis* (basis, supposition)
MEANING: Statement not proved but assumed to be true for purposes of argument or further study or investigation
CONTEXT: "The *hypothesis* was formulated after several detectives had pieced together a plausible motive for the crime."
SYNONYMS: premise, theory, postulate
OTHER FORMS: hypothetical (adj.), hypothesize (v.)

acrid (adj) (ˈak-rəd)

ORIGIN: Latin *acer* (sharp)
MEANING: Sharp, biting, or irritating to the senses
CONTEXT: "The *acrid* smoke from the fire was so irritating that most of the spectators soon left."
SYNONYMS: pungent, corrosive, caustic, bitter
ANTONYMS: insipid, flat, mild
OTHER FORMS: acridity (n.), acridness (n.), acridly (adv.)

A. Circle the letter of the best meaning for each vocabulary word.

1. acrid: a) hard b) bitter c) miserly d) false
2. hypothesis: a) fact b) theory c) knowledge d) injection needle
3. hypothetical: a) convalescent b) assumed c) destroyed d) dreamed
4. acridness: a) dryness b) bitterness c) hatred d) rigor
5. reprieve: a) punishment b) attack c) delay d) falsehood

B. Supply the proper form of the most appropriate vocabulary word.

1. The detective could not gather sufficient evidence to support the ____________________.
2. The ____________________ taste of the spoiled lemon juice made her mouth pucker.
3. "Since you cannot ____________________ the crabgrass, you must learn to live with it," remarked the gardener.
4. The history teacher asked her class to think about a(n) ____________________ discussion between Eleanor Roosevelt and Thomas Jefferson.
5. When removed from the *(surroundings)* ____________________ of the speech, the politician's remarks were misleading.
6. The ____________________ of the fumes from the chemistry experiment irritated Becky's nose.

Lesson 42

coercion (n) (kō-'ər-zhən)

ORIGIN: Latin *coercere* (hold in) + *ion* (action or condition)
MEANING: The exercise of force or power to compel an act or choice
CONTEXT: "The militants used *coercion* to get information from the prisoner."
SYNONYMS: compulsion, constraint
OTHER FORMS: coerce (v.), coercive (adj.)

lottery (n) ('lȧt-ə-rē)

ORIGIN: Old English *hlot* (lot)
MEANING: Any scheme for making selections or for distributing prizes by chance
CONTEXT: "Write your name on the paper and drop it in the box; next Saturday, the winner will be chosen at the *lottery*."
SYNONYMS: gamble, raffle

A. Circle the letter of the word that best completes each analogy.

1. religion: theologian : : ________: gambler
   a) protocol b) hypothesis c) lottery d) rifle
2. plausible: credible : : ________: caustic
   a) hypothetical b) coughing c) acrid d) plastic
3. gloat: exult : : ________: compel
   a) exhilarate b) wrest c) coerce d) relinquish
4. belief: truth : : ________: postulate
   a) proof b) hypothesis c) theology d) premiere

B. Supply the proper form of the most appropriate vocabulary word.

1. Dictators often use ________________ to get subjects to do things they do not want to do.
2. The totalitarian government ________________ the peasants to form collective farms.
3. The ________________ reek of the gas caused Bruce to sneeze and cough.
4. When Ida won a sports car in the ________________ after buying only one 25-cent ticket, her faith in luck was restored.

Lesson 43

fluctuation (n) (ˌflək-chə-ˈwā-shən)

ORIGIN: Latin *fluctuatus* (wavering)
MEANING: Continual change from one condition, position, or course to another
CONTEXT: "The *fluctuation* in daily temperature these last weeks has made it hard to know how to dress."
SYNONYMS: waver, undulation, vacillation, oscillation
ANTONYMS: steadiness, resolution
OTHER FORM: fluctuate (v.)

eccentric (adj) (ik-ˈsen-trik)

ORIGIN: Greek *ekkentr* (out of center)
MEANING: Being different from some established pattern
CONTEXT: "Judging by his unusual dress and conduct, I gather he is quite an *eccentric* person."
SYNONYMS: idiosyncratic, unusual, peculiar, singular
ANTONYMS: conventional, usual
OTHER FORMS: eccentrically (adv.), eccentricity (n.), eccentric (n.)

A. Circle the letter of the best meaning for each vocabulary word.

1. eccentric: a) sharpened b) unpublished c) unusual d) conventional
2. fluctuation: a) invitation b) sales talk c) river d) wavering
3. lottery: a) excess b) litter c) raffle d) speech
4. coerce: a) sell b) compel c) condemn d) hate
5. eccentricity: a) whirlwind b) speed c) expectation d) peculiarity

B. Supply the proper form of the most appropriate vocabulary word.

1. The stock market will normally ____________________ as the political situation in Washington changes.
2. ____________________ in tidal levels affect the clamming industry in the state of Maine.
3. Impatient parents sometimes use ____________________ to make a naughty child behave.
4. The ____________________ family lived in a dusty, boarded-up house for forty years without once receiving any visitors.
5. The stranger sold tickets for a(n) ____________________ that advertised exciting prizes, but she left town with the funds before announcing any winners.

Lesson 44

cede mov

-cede- (root)

ORIGIN: Latin *cedere* (to go)
MEANING: To move or to go
CONTEXT: "re*cede*"
OTHER FORMS: -ceed- (ex*ceed*), -ced- (pro*ced*ure), -cess- (suc*cess*)

-mov- (root)

ORIGIN: Latin *movere* (to move)
MEANING: To set in motion
CONTEXT: "*mov*able"
OTHER FORMS: -mot- (*mot*ion), -mob- (*mob*ile)

A. In each of the italicized words below, underline the word parts that you have learned. Then, using your knowledge of the meanings of the word parts, circle the letter of the best meaning for the italicized word. (For some words there may be only one word part.)

1. *intercede* in prayer: a) go between b) take away c) abandon d) gaze upward
2. *remove* the stain: a) eliminate b) set c) recognize d) dislike
3. textbook for *parapsychology:* a) building design b) dramatic pantomimes c) study of mental telepathy d) paratrooper maneuver
4. state's decision to *secede:* a) join b) break away c) tax d) capture
5. *movable* parts: a) capable of being nailed b) capable of being shifted c) capable of being assembled d) capable of being developed
6. *excess* glue: a) sticky b) effective c) overflowing d) borrowed
7. *automotive* repair: a) expensive b) vehicle c) planned c) unfinished
8. travel *incognito:* a) unfair b) not recognized or known c) captured d) quick
9. *mobility* of sales staff: a) salary b) transferability c) quality d) loyalty
10. *precede* the attack: a) come between b) go before c) organize d) unify

B. REVIEW: Write one sentence for each of the following words. Each sentence must be complete enough to indicate the meaning of the vocabulary word through context clues and must not simply be an adaptation of a sentence in this book.

1. acrid 2. coercion 3. hypothesis 4. eradicate 5. lottery
6. fluctuation 7. stupor 8. eccentric 9. nurture 10. diverse

Lesson 45

annihilate (v) (ə-ˈnī-ə-ˌlāt)

ORIGIN: Latin *annihilat* (brought to nothing)
MEANING: To reduce to utter ruin or destroy entirely
CONTEXT: "During World War II, whole sections of cities in Germany, England, and France were completely *annihilated* by bombing."
SYNONYMS: obliterate, devastate, ravage, nullify, abolish, eradicate
ANTONYMS: create, preserve
OTHER FORMS: annihilative (adj.), annihilatory (adj.), annihilation (n.)

nautical (adj) (ˈnȯt-i-kəl)

ORIGIN: Latin *nautic* (pertaining to ships or sailors)
MEANING: Pertaining to sailors, ships, or navigation
CONTEXT: "I did not understand the *nautical* terms used by the navy captain."
SYNONYM: maritime

A. Circle the letter of the word that best completes each analogy.

1. relinquish: surrender : : _______: obliterate
   a) equivocate b) preserve c) annihilate d) wrest
2. eccentric: idiosyncratic : : _______: maritime
   a) nautical b) knotted c) conforming d) gay
3. fluctuating: steady : : _______: conventional
   a) convening b) undulating c) edifying d) eccentric
4. connive: scheme : : _______: waver
   a) water b) coerce c) fluctuate d) condone

B. Supply the proper form of the most appropriate vocabulary word.

1. The ________________ odor of the dense smog irritated everyone in the downtown area.
2. The ________________ of an entire platoon during a night raid lowered the morale of every recruit in the company.
3. Mrs. Wong and her son *(schemed)* ________________ to keep Margie's birthday present an absolute secret.
4. Distance on the ocean is measured in ________________ miles.
5. The hurricane ________________ all the summer homes along the beachfront.

Lesson 46

conjure (v) (kȧn-ˈjər)

ORIGIN: Latin *conjurare* (to swear)
MEANING: To create or bring about as if by magic
CONTEXT: "Billy, having no one to play with, *conjured* up a playmate whom he called Manuel."
SYNONYMS: imagine, charm, hallucinate (see below)
OTHER FORM: conjurer (n.)

hallucination (n) (hə-ˌlüs-n-ˈā-shən)

ORIGIN: Latin *hallucinatio* (a wandering of the mind)
MEANING: Seeing objects or visions that do not exist outside the mind
CONTEXT: "During the illness, he suffered from *hallucinations* in which he thought he saw his dead brother."
SYNONYMS: illusion, delusion, phantasm, mirage
ANTONYM: reality
OTHER FORMS: hallucinate (v.), hallucinatory (adj.)

A. Circle the letter of the word that best completes each analogy.

1. nurture: foster : : _______: imagine

   a) eradicate b) surprise c) debilitate d) hallucinate

2. eradicate: efface : : _______: imagine

   a) exercise b) destroy c) conjure d) coerce

3. slovenly: fastidious : : _______: created

   a) perverse b) meticulous c) annihilated d) rampant

B. Supply the proper form of the most appropriate vocabulary word.

1. To end World War II, the United States ________________ most of Hiroshima by dropping an atomic bomb on the city.
2. When Murray's fever hit 103°, he began to have ________________ about an enchanted desert.
3. The witches in Shakespeare's *Macbeth* ________________ up the spirits of the future with a magical brew.
4. When I realized that my ________________ were not real, my psychiatrist told me that I was getting better.
5. The tricks of the ________________ were the hit of the traveling road show.

fester (v) ('fes-tər)

ORIGIN: Latin *fistula* (ulcer)
MEANING: To grow more acute and harder to bear; to become more irritating; in an infection, to form pus
CONTEXT: "Without proper medical treatment, the wound in his leg *festered*."
SYNONYM: ulcerate
ANTONYMS: pacify, ease

atrocious (adj) (ə-'trō-shəs)

ORIGIN: Latin *atroci* (fierce)
MEANING: Extremely wicked or cruel; dreadful
CONTEXT: "The *atrocious* behavior of those two youths deserves severe punishment."
SYNONYMS: felonious, devilish, detestable, outrageous
ANTONYMS: pleasing, good
OTHER FORMS: atrocity (n.), atrociousness (n.), atrociously (adv.)

A. Circle the letter of the best meaning for each vocabulary word.

1. conjure: a) condole b) imagine c) connive d) pacify
2. atrocious: a) rankling b) pleasing c) outrageous d) huge
3. fester: a) ulcerate b) eradicate c) surmise d) ease
4. annihilate: a) fester b) obliterate c) console d) construct
5. hallucination: a) delusion b) nurturance c) edification d) stupor
6. atrociousness: a) temper b) outrageousness c) consummation d) fatigue

B. Supply the proper form of the most appropriate vocabulary word.

1. The ________________ conditions in the refugee camp reduced the inhabitants to a starving, desperate state.
2. The shrapnel wound became infected and began to ________________ without a medic's attention.
3. "The ________________ committed in the name of religion are the work of the devil," shouted the minister angrily.
4. Although at first Maria did not complain about the unjust treatment, the anger that ________________ within her soon prompted her to rebel.
5. The best part of the show occurred when the magician ________________ a rabbit out of a hat for the children in the audience.

Lesson 48

chastise (v) (cha-ˈstīz)

ORIGIN: Middle English *chastisen* (to chasten)
MEANING: To inflict punishment on; to censure severely
CONTEXT: "To *chastise* children severely, especially by corporal punishment, is seldom good discipline."
SYNONYMS: reprimand, punish, flog, castigate
ANTONYMS: absolve, reward, excuse
OTHER FORM: chastisement (n.)

remuneration (n) (ri-myü-nə-ˈrā-shən)

ORIGIN: Latin *remuneratio* (to give or reward)
MEANING: That which rewards or pays
CONTEXT: "She received little *remuneration* for all the services she performed."
SYNONYMS: recompense, reimbursement, payment
ANTONYM: penalty
OTHER FORMS: remunerative (adj.), remunerate (v.)

A. Circle the letter of the word that best completes each analogy.

1. convalesce: recuperate : : ________: chastise
   a) purify b) surmise c) capture d) punish
2. bungle: mishandle : : ________: imagine
   a) delve b) forget c) hallucinate d) detect
3. separate: segregate : : ________: remunerate
   a) relinquish b) remember c) unify d) reimburse
4. intimate: hint : : ________: ulcerate
   a) fasten b) confide c) ease d) fester

B. Supply the proper form of the most appropriate vocabulary word.

1. The treasurer reminded the members that they had agreed to ____________ any guest speaker.
2. The indolent student was ____________ by the disciplinary council.
3. Even though the ____________ for Raoul's hard work was regrettably small, he enjoyed supervising the project and appreciated the praise for his successful efforts.
4. "If you do not correct the error of your ways, God will ____________ you all," the prophet warned the wicked nation.
5. Mr. Tucci was appalled by the ____________ behavior of his rowdy houseguests.

multi- (prefix)

ORIGIN: Latin *multus* (many)
MEANING: More than one, many
CONTEXT: "*multi*millionaire"
NOTE: You will also want to learn *poly-*, another Latin prefix meaning "many," as in "*poly*gamy."

-plic- (root)

ORIGIN: Latin *plicare* (to fold)
MEANING: To fold
CONTEXT: "com*plic*ated"
OTHER FORM: -pli- (*pli*able)

A. In each of the italicized words below, underline the word parts that you have learned. Then, using your knowledge of the meanings of the word parts, circle the letter of the best meaning for the italicized word. (For some words there may be only one word part.)

1. *pliant* metal: a) hard b) complex c) bendable d) surplus
2. *multifarious* collection: a) limited b) handmade c) diverse d) coin
3. *interpose* a remark: a) punctuate b) explain c) insert d) ignore
4. *complicate* the issue: a) simplify b) debate c) entangle d) vote for
5. *multitudinous* factors: a) selected b) narrow c) many d) involved
6. *polytheism* of native tribes: a) ignorance b) progressivism c) worshiping of many gods d) practice of witchcraft
7. *accomplice* to crime: a) one who is involved with others b) obstacle that stands in the way c) acceptable excuse d) speech in support
8. *procession* of clowns: a) makeup b) training c) parade d) laughter

B. REVIEW: Write one sentence for each of the following words. Each sentence must be complete enough to indicate the meaning of the vocabulary word through context clues and must not simply be an adaptation of a sentence in this book.

1. fester 2. remuneration 3. nautical 4. atrocious 5. annihilate
6. conjure 7. chastise 8. fluctuation 9. hallucination 10. eccentric

lenient (adj) ('lē-nē-ənt)

ORIGIN: Latin *lenire* (softening, soothing)
MEANING: Indulgent, gently tolerant, permissive
CONTEXT: "Mother tended to be *lenient* toward us children, while Father was more harsh in his discipline."
SYNONYMS: easy, gentle, forebearing, long-suffering
ANTONYMS: harsh, cruel, merciless, stern, rigorous
OTHER FORMS: leniency (n.), leniently (adv.)

bequeath (v) (bi-'kwēth)

ORIGIN: Old English *becwethan* (to say)
MEANING: To hand down; to dispose of by last will
CONTEXT: "Before her death, my grandmother *bequeathed* to me a cameo necklace that had been in the family for years."
SYNONYMS: will, transfer, give, leave, pass on
OTHER FORMS: bequest (n.), bequeathment (n.)

A. Circle the letter of the word that best completes each analogy.

1. lax: indolent : : _______ : indulgent
   a) vigorous b) lenient c) stuporous d) surmised
2. nurture: food : : _______ : dynamite
   a) edify b) transform c) annihilate d) swab
3. wrest: extract : : _______ : will
   a) wring b) condone c) secrete d) bequeath
4. stuporous: sleepy : : _______ : dreadful
   a) lenient b) urchin c) atrocious d) rigorous

B. Supply the proper form of the most appropriate vocabulary word.

1. Mr. Swanscot made his niece an heiress by _______________ to her real estate and industrial investments worth over $3,000,000.
2. Bob's _______________ parents did not reprimand him when he forgot to lock the front door.
3. Public _______________ of a criminal was once a common practice.
4. John could easily confide in his parents because of their tolerance and _______________.
5. When Anita Adams died, her _______________ to the college amounted to $400,000 in securities.

Lesson 51

appendage (n) (ə-ˈpən-dij)

ORIGIN: Late Latin *appendire* (to hang)
MEANING: Something attached to a larger or more important thing
CONTEXT: "The arms and legs are the *appendages* of the human body."
SYNONYMS: appurtenance, adjunct, attachment, addition
OTHER FORMS: append (v.), appendaged (adj.), appendix (n.)

timely (adj) (ˈtīm-lē)

ORIGIN: Old English *timlic* (time)
MEANING: Occurring at a suitable time; well-timed
CONTEXT: "The book entitled *The Universe* is a *timely* addition to Michael's library because he is so interested in space exploration right now."
SYNONYMS: opportune, seasonable, appropriate
ANTONYMS: untimely, inopportune, inappropriate
OTHER FORM: timeliness (n.)

A. Circle the letter of the best meaning for each vocabulary word.

1. timely: a) musical b) opportune c) quick d) changing
2. appendage: a) glue b) rope c) edifice d) attachment
3. lenient: a) tottering b) tired c) tolerant d) indolent
4. timeliness: a) appropriateness b) condolence c) convalescence d) edification
5. bequest: a) search b) question c) gift d) problem
6. append: a) turn over b) offend c) extend d) add

B. Supply the proper form of the most appropriate vocabulary word.

1. Louise's investment in the electronics industry was ____________________; shortly thereafter, her stock doubled in value.
2. Mr. Samuel ____________________ his meager possessions to the state of Florida, since he had received state welfare checks for twenty-three years.
3. The crab has eight ____________________ attached to its abdomen.
4. Since the off-Broadway show was on the verge of closing, the ____________________ of the favorable review was remarkable.
5. The editors decided to ____________________ an index to the end of the book.
6. "Considering how much more work Olive did than Sandy, it is unfair to give the two equal ____________________," complained the project supervisor to the treasurer.

Lesson 52

Hilarious · Bane

hilarious (adj) (hil-'ar-ē-əs)

ORIGIN: Latin *hilaris* (cheerful)
MEANING: Arousing boisterous merriment or gaiety
CONTEXT: "The *hilarious* antics of the clowns aroused much laughter and applause among the spectators at the circus."
SYNONYMS: mirthful, gleeful, exuberant, jocund, jocular
ANTONYMS: glum, morose, cheerless, somber
OTHER FORMS: hilarity (n.), hilariousness (n.), hilariously (adv.)

bane (n) (bān)

ORIGIN: Old English *bana* (slayer)
MEANING: That which ruins, harms, or kills
CONTEXT: "The witch doctor's curse became the *bane* of the superstitious chieftain's life."
SYNONYMS: curse, adversity, affliction, torment, scourge
ANTONYMS: remedy, fortune

A. Circle the letter of the word that best completes each analogy.

1. rigorous: stringent : : ______: mirthful

   a) tormented b) strong c) hilarious d) morose

2. eccentric: idiosyncratic : : ______: opportune

   a) inappropriate b) central c) timely d) operated

3. lottery: raffle : : ______: scourge

   a) wish b) bane c) darkness d) coercion

4. coercion: compulsion : : ______: addition

   a) constraint b) appendix c) remuneration d) reprieve

B. Supply the proper form of the most appropriate vocabulary word.

1. Her alcoholic husband was the ______________ of my great-aunt's existence.
2. The (*added part*) ______________ to the book was not included in the last edition.
3. Beethoven's deafness was the ______________ of his life as a musician.
4. The boisterous laughter aroused by the ______________ of Jack's pantomime was cut short when the teacher unexpectedly entered the room.
5. Roberto's remark about the coming party was not very ______________ since Joanna has not yet been invited.

coherent (adj) (kō-'hir-ənt)

ORIGIN: Latin *cohaere* (to stick)
MEANING: Having the quality of holding firmly together; having a natural or logical connection
CONTEXT: "The speaker rambled along and never presented a *coherent* statement of his position on the issues."
SYNONYMS: cohesive, adherent, consistent
ANTONYM: incoherent
OTHER FORMS: cohere (v.), coherence (n.), coherently (adv.)

stipulate (v) ('stip-yə-ˌlāt)

ORIGIN: Latin *stipulatus* (to demand terms in an agreement)
MEANING: To make a specific demand
CONTEXT: "Our agreement with the contractor *stipulates* that he must finish the job by July."
SYNONYMS: specify, demand, contract
OTHER FORMS: stipulation (n.), stipulatory (adj.)

A. Circle the letter of the best meaning for each vocabulary word.

1. hilarity: a) height b) fluctuation c) mirthfulness d) hilly
2. stipulate: a) specify b) decide c) sharpen d) anger
3. coherent: a) lax b) slippery c) polite d) cohesive
4. bane: a) prevention b) rule c) curse d) argument
5. coherence: a) propriety b) addition c) vigor d) consistency
6. stipulation: a) demand b) turn c) inflation d) pretense

B. Supply the proper form of the most appropriate vocabulary word.

1. The accident victim walked around in a daze, mumbling things that were not at all ________________.
2. "That's ________________," shrieked Elsa, holding her sides in laughter.
3. The outline of Mary's research paper showed ________________ organization and logical development of her ideas.
4. Fleas are the ________________ of a dog's existence.
5. The governor ________________ that, in return for funds for urban development, the city would have to increase taxes.

Lesson 54

dict loqu

-dict- (root)

ORIGIN: Latin *dictare* (to say)
MEANING: To say, command, speak, word
CONTEXT: "contra*dict*ion"
OTHER FORM: -dic- (in*dic*ate)

-loqu- (root)

ORIGIN: Latin *loqui* (to speak)
MEANING: To say, speak, talk
CONTEXT: "e*loqu*ent"
OTHER FORMS: -locu- (*locu*tion), -lecu- (e*lecu*tion), -logue- (pro*logue*)

A. In each of the italicized words below, underline the word parts that you have learned. Then, using your knowledge of the meanings of the word parts, circle the letter of the best meaning for the italicized word. (For some words there may be only one word part.)

1. *loquacious* comedian: a) hilarious b) talkative c) effective d) hired
2. *epilogue* of a play: a) production b) scenery c) final speech d) plot
3. office *dictaphone:* a) secretarial pool b) voice recorder c) copier d) manager
4. interesting *colloquy:* a) sale b) collection c) conversation d) race
5. weather *prediction:* a) map b) vane c) forecast d) front
6. childish *interlocution:* a) games b) mystery c) conversation d) logic
7. prophet's *precognition:* a) foreknowledge b) robe c) mystery d) importance
8. issue an *edict:* a) new stamp b) proclamation c) law d) written message
9. *abdicate* the throne: a) ascend b) fight over c) renounce d) dream of
10. unnecessary *circumlocution:* a) circumstances b) locations c) problems d) evasion in speech

B. REVIEW: Write one sentence for each of the following words. Each sentence must be complete enough to indicate the meaning of the vocabulary word through context clues and must not be simply an adaptation of a sentence in this book.

1. bane
2. stipulate
3. hilarious
4. remuneration
5. coherent
6. atrocious
7. lenient
8. appendage
9. edify
10. bequeath

alien (n) (ˈā-lē-ən)

ORIGIN: Latin *alienus* (other)
MEANING: One born in or belonging to another country
CONTEXT: "Many *aliens* become citizens of this country after living here for seven years."
SYNONYMS: immigrant, foreigner, stranger
ANTONYM: native
OTHER FORMS: alienation (n.), alienate (v.), alien (adj.)

vehemence (n) (ˈvē-ə-mən[t]s)

ORIGIN: Latin *vehementia* (vehement)
MEANING: Intense emotion, violence, fury
CONTEXT: "The *vehemence* of the attack against the sales tax created an equal amount of zeal among the tax's supporters."
SYNONYMS: violence, intensity, impetuosity
ANTONYMS: coolness, impassivity, stolidness
OTHER FORMS: vehement (adj.), vehemently (adv.)

A. Circle the letter of the best meaning for each vocabulary word.

1. alien: a) traveler b) friend c) sales clerk d) stranger
2. alienation: a) urbanity b) rigor c) separation d) hatred
3. vehement: a) poisonous b) stolid c) solid d) violent
4. vehemence: a) pertness b) irritation c) intensity d) support
5. cohere: a) adhere b) repair c) listen d) send

B. Supply the proper form of the most appropriate vocabulary word.

1. All ________________ must register with the United States government once a year.
2. When Senator Howard's political views were attacked by his opponent, he called a press conference to issue a(n) ________________ defense of his positions.
3. The clique at the high school ________________ most students because of its snobbish attitude toward everyone not in the group.
4. The impetuous child ________________ stamped her foot when her mother suggested it was time for an afternoon nap.
5. The father's refusal to respect his son's privacy resulted in the boy's ________________ from his parents.

gad (v) (gad)

ORIGIN: Middle English *gadden* (wanderer or vagabond)
MEANING: To be on the go to little purpose
CONTEXT: "I *gadded* about town this morning and accomplished very little of importance."
SYNONYMS: roam, wander, meander, traipse, saunter, jaunt

indelible (adj) (in-'del-ə-bəl)

ORIGIN: Latin *indelebil* (indestructible)
MEANING: Incapable of being removed, washed away, or erased
CONTEXT: "If that is *indelible* ink on your shirt, I will not be able to get it out."
SYNONYMS: fixed, permanent
ANTONYMS: eradicable, eradicative, erasable
OTHER FORMS: indelibility (n.), indelibleness (n.), indelibly (adv.)

A. Circle the letter of the best meaning for each vocabulary word.

1. indelible: a) doubting b) eradicable c) fixed d) unpersuaded
2. gad: a) anger b) wander c) dress d) repair
3. bane: a) prevention b) scourge c) vanity d) aid
4. vehemence: a) fury b) movement c) buttress d) thought
5. gad: a) traipse b) exchange c) plan d) rotate
6. indelibly: a) frankly b) falsely c) permanently d) easily

B. Supply the proper form of the most appropriate vocabulary word.

1. "You're nothing but a(n) ____________________-about," scolded my father, who was upset by my constant wanderings about the country.
2. The traditional Polish customs were ____________________ to the American tourist.
3. Catherine's amusing account of her ____________________ encounter with the sales clerk who acted exactly like Gilda Radner brightened the evening immensely.
4. ____________________ ink cannot be removed.
5. A large group of college students ____________________ about the country during the summer, attending every major jazz festival.
6. The cleaning fluid was very effective except in removing ____________________ stains.

attune (v) (ə-'t[y]ün)

ORIGIN: Latin *at* or *ad* (at) + *tonus* (tension or tone)
MEANING: To adjust; to bring into harmony or sympathetic relationship
CONTEXT: "Although he was accustomed to living in the countryside, he has *attuned* himself to city life."
SYNONYMS: tune, harmonize, adapt, acclimatize
ANTONYM: maladjust

genial (adj) ('jē-nyəl)

ORIGIN: Latin *genialis* (jovial, pleasant)
MEANING: Being cheerful, cordial, or kindly
CONTEXT: "Being a man of *genial* disposition, the host soon made everyone feel welcome and at ease."
SYNONYMS: agreeable, friendly, pleasant, gracious
ANTONYMS: sullen, cool, unfriendly
OTHER FORMS: genially (adv.), geniality (n.), genialness (n.)

A. Circle the letter of the best meaning for each vocabulary word.

1. genial: a) intelligent b) sexy c) glum d) agreeable
2. attune: a) fascinate b) adapt c) climb d) make
3. gad: a) provoke b) roam c) exhilarate d) sell
4. geniality: a) graciousness b) unpleasantness c) originality d) involvement
5. indelible: a) printed b) permanent c) black d) doubtful
6. attune: a) tune b) turn c) time d) teach

B. Supply the proper form of the most appropriate vocabulary word.

1. The popular hostess extended a(n) ________________ welcome to her guests.
2. After Danny became ________________ to the schedule at nursery school, he looked forward to going every day.
3. "The sooner our company is ________________ to the demands of the marketplace, the sooner we will make money," said the executive.
4. The ________________ of the woman's angry reply surprised her friends since she was usually quite calm.
5. Before Chris left for camp, he wrote his name in all his clothes with a(n) ________________ pen so they would not be lost in the laundry.

Lesson 58

tract volv

-tract- (root)

ORIGIN: Latin *tractum* (to draw)
MEANING: To draw, drag, or pull
CONTEXT: "*tract*or"

-volv- (root)

ORIGIN: Latin *volvere* (to roll)
MEANING: To roll or turn
CONTEXT: "re*volv*e"
OTHER FORMS: -volu- (re*volu*tion), -vol- (fri*vol*ous)

Sarah Frank

A. In each of the italicized words below, underline the word parts that you have learned. Then, using your knowledge of the meanings of the word parts, circle the letter of the best meaning for the italicized words. (For some words there may be only one word part.)

1. *evolve* an idea: a) reason out b) ignore c) produce d) squelch
2. *receding* shore line: a) constant b) beautiful c) retreating d) predictable
3. *attract* specialists: a) consult with b) draw c) observe d) pay
4. *extract* an object: a) confuse b) pull out c) transform d) recognize
5. *voluble* gadget: a) peculiar b) illogical c) rotating d) handy
6. *dictatorial* personality: a) commanding others b) infuriating others c) impressing others d) ignoring others
7. *devolve* responsibility: a) hand down b) accept c) reward d) acknowledge
8. *retract* the statement: a) profess b) withdraw c) print d) repeat
9. a *colloquial* tone: a) musical b) piercing c) conversational d) steady
10. *contracting* metal: a) used to hold things in place b) drawing or pulling together c) used in construction work d) of superior quality

B. REVIEW: Write one sentence for each of the following words. Each sentence must be complete enough to indicate the meaning of the vocabulary word through context clues and must not simply be an adaptation of a sentence in this book.

1. genial 2. bane 3. attune 4. fester 5. gad
6. vehemence 7. stipulate 8. indelible 9. coherent 10. alien

Lesson 59

effigy (n) ('ef-ə-jē)

ORIGIN: Latin *effigia* (shape, form)
MEANING: A crude representation of someone, often used for purposes of ridicule
CONTEXT: "The angry students created an *effigy* of the dean whom they disliked."
SYNONYMS: figure, model, representation, image

amorous (adj) ('am-[ə]-rəs)

ORIGIN: Latin *amoras* (love)
MEANING: Inclined to love; relating to or caused by love, especially sexual love
CONTEXT: "Since he is an *amorous* person, John falls in love with any girl he dates."
SYNONYMS: loving, fond, passionate, enamored
ANTONYMS: indifferent, cold
OTHER FORMS: amorousness (n.), amorously (adv.), amour (n.)

A. Circle the letter of the best meaning for each vocabulary word.

1. effigy: a) rudeness b) building c) representation d) benefit
2. amorous: a) stupid b) talkative c) loving d) leaning
3. edify: a) uplift b) ridicule c) demonstrate d) stipulate
4. connive: a) console b) conspire c) scorn d) wait
5. amorousness: a) dependency b) amorality c) passion d) politeness

B. Supply the proper form of the most appropriate vocabulary word.

1. Mike's ________________ girlfriend came running from the plane and threw her arms around his neck.
2. ________________ of the hated general were carried mockingly through the streets on the night of the national elections.
3. Eleanora carefully ________________ her delicate plants through the cold, dreary winter.
4. ________________ of the tribe's enemies were hung in the fields as scarecrows.
5. There are several ________________ scenes in the romantic movie.

Lesson 60

listless (adj) (ˈlist-ləs)

ORIGIN: Old English *lystan* (to please) + *leas* (without)
MEANING: Feeling no inclination toward or interest in anything
CONTEXT: "John's *listless* behavior led his mother to wonder if he might be ill."
SYNONYMS: lethargic, lassitudinous, languid, stuporous, apathetic
ANTONYMS: animated, exhilarated, exuberant
OTHER FORMS: listlessly (adv.), listlessness (n.)

rostrum (n) (ˈrȧs-trəm)

ORIGIN: Latin *rostrum* (speaker's platform decorated with the beaks of captured ships)
MEANING: A platform or stage for public speaking, a pulpit
CONTEXT: "As the speaker walked up to the *rostrum,* she was greeted by an outburst of applause."
SYNONYMS: stage, platform

A. Circle the letter of the word that best completes each analogy.

1. genially: pleasantly : : ______: languidly
   a) frankly b) enviously c) listlessly d) softly
2. edifice: building : : ______: platform
   a) effigy b) rostrum c) planting d) gesticulation
3. aesthetics: beauty : : ______: image
   a) edifice b) stipulation c) effigy d) nurturance
4. rigorous: lenient : : ______: indifferent
   a) cold b) surmised c) conjured d) amorous

B. Supply the proper form of the most appropriate vocabulary word.

1. The ______________ was decorated with yellow mums for the speaker's address.
2. ______________ of persons who worked with the enemy hung in the public square as a warning of what would happen when the traitors were caught.
3. The dignitaries were seated on the ______________, each awaiting his turn to speak.
4. The young child *(cringed)* ______________ before the enormous dog that stood barking at the gate.
5. Amy's letters to her fiancé were ______________ and sentimental.
6. Bored by the summer routine, Larry lounged ______________ on the front porch.

Lesson 61

staunch (adj) (stȯnch)

ORIGIN: Middle French *estancher* (to stand)
MEANING: Firm or steadfast in principle; loyal; substantial
CONTEXT: "If I ever need help, I know that I can call on Ruth because she is a *staunch* friend."
SYNONYMS: stalwart, resolute, unswerving
ANTONYMS: irresolute, unfaithful
OTHER FORMS: staunchness (n.), staunchly (adv.)

larceny (n) (ˈlärs-nē)

ORIGIN: Latin *latrocir* (robbery)
MEANING: The unlawful taking away of a person's property; theft
CONTEXT: "The youths were charged with grand *larceny* after they were found driving Mr. Rojas's car."
SYNONYMS: robbery, thievery
OTHER FORM: larcenist (n.)

A. Circle the letter of the word that best completes each analogy.

1. irresolute: unfaithful : : _______: loyal
   a) royal b) staunch c) genial d) lenient
2. indelible: permanent : : _______: lethargic
   a) unquestioned b) listless c) amorous d) coherent
3. arena: bullfighter : : _______: speaker
   a) roster b) rostrum c) religion d) routine
4. atrocity: wickedness : : _______: theft
   a) bane b) remuneration c) effigy d) larceny

B. Supply the proper form of the most appropriate vocabulary word.

1. When Cheryl ran for treasurer, she relied on her pals to be _______________ supporters.
2. When the boy was caught stealing hubcaps, he was charged with _______________.
3. Lying _______________ in bed, the patient responded to none of our attempts to amuse him.
4. The loyal diplomatic aide _______________ supported her colleague when he was accused of espionage.
5. Shoplifting is petty _______________.

Lesson 62

squall (n) (skwȯl)

ORIGIN:	Probably Scandinavian origin *skval* (useless chatter, rushing water)
MEANING 1:	A hoarse cry
CONTEXT 1:	"The mother came running as soon as the infant emitted the first *squall*."
MEANING 2:	A sudden violent weather disturbance
CONTEXT 2:	"Since it looks as if we may have a *squall*, you shouldn't take out the boat today."
SYNONYMS:	scream, yell; storm

rational (adj) ('rash-nəl)

ORIGIN:	Latin *ratio* (reason) + *alis* (equal)
MEANING:	Having or exercising reason; sensible
CONTEXT:	"The Campus Committee has worked out a *rational* parking plan for students and faculty."
SYNONYMS:	reasonable, sane, natural
ANTONYMS:	irrational, unreasonable, unwise
OTHER FORMS:	rationally (adv.), rationality (n.)

A. Circle the letter of the word in each group that does not belong.

1. a) sane b) sensible c) rational d) unreasonable
2. a) stalwart b) unswerving c) irresolute d) staunch
3. a) silence b) peace c) squall d) quietude
4. a) theft b) robbery c) squall d) larceny
5. a) scream b) squall c) yell d) decide

B. Supply the proper form of the most appropriate vocabulary word.

1. Ms. Johnson's arguments in favor of tax reform were ________________ and persuasive.
2. The sudden appearance of black, billowing clouds on the horizon warned us to expect a(n) ________________.
3. When the gems disappeared, the chauffeur was held on suspicion of ________________.
4. Since most of the original supporters abandoned the cause, Robert's continued ________________ support was noteworthy.
5. Although the reclusive scientist could always give a(n) ________________ explanation for his behavior, many people consider him strange.

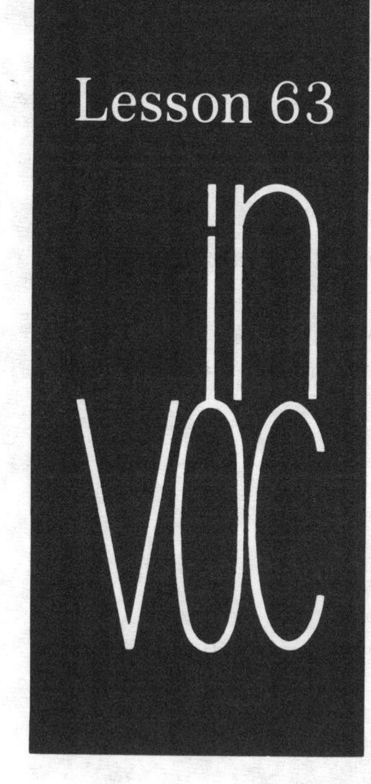

in- (prefix)

ORIGIN: Latin *in* (not, into)
MEANING 1: Not
CONTEXT 1: "*in*correct"
MEANING 2: In, into, within
CONTEXT 2: "*in*hale"
OTHER FORMS: il- (*il*legal), im- (*im*pulse), ir- (*ir*rigate)

-voc- (root)

ORIGIN: Latin *vox* (voice)
MEANING: To call
CONTEXT: "*voc*al"
OTHER FORM: -vok- (re*vok*e)

A. In each of the italicized words below, underline the word parts that you have learned. Then, using your knowledge of the meanings of the word parts, circle the letter of the best meaning for the italicized word. (For some words there may be only one word part.)

1. *impious* joke: a) funny b) unreligious c) good d) complicated
2. *irreparable* damage: a) caused by neglect b) not able to be fixed c) reported too late d) caused by war
3. *equivocal* answer: a) wrong b) unclearly stated c) hoped for d) clear
4. *vociferous* assembly: a) children's meeting b) characterized by noisy shouts c) made up of many people d) holding the interest of the students
5. *imperturbed* sleep: a) not disturbed b) taking place in the morning c) bothered d) continuous
6. *incredible* excuse: a) plausible b) helpful c) not believable d) good
7. choose a *vocation:* a) representative b) menu c) calling d) policy
8. *inconspicuous* girl: a) amorous b) fashionable c) prepared d) not noticeable

B. REVIEW: Write one sentence for each of the following words. Each sentence must be complete enough to indicate the meaning of the vocabulary word through context clues and must not simply be an adaptation of a sentence in this book.

1. larceny 2. rational 3. staunch 4. rostrum 5. genial
6. squall 7. listless 8. amorous 9. attune 10. effigy

Lesson 64

fray inalienable

fray (v) (frā)

ORIGIN: Latin *fricare* (to rub)
MEANING: To wear by rubbing; to separate the threads at the edge
CONTEXT: "The cuffs of his jacket began to *fray* before it went out of style."
SYNONYMS: frazzle, tatter
ANTONYM: mend
OTHER FORM: frayed (adj.)

inalienable (adj) (in-ˈāl-yə-nə-bəl)

ORIGIN: French *in* (not) + *alienable* (transferable)
MEANING: Incapable of being surrendered or transferred
CONTEXT: "Although liberty is said to be an *inalienable* right, many are deprived of it."
SYNONYMS: unforfeitable, unimpeachable, sacrosanct, sacred
ANTONYMS: alienable, forfeitable, impeachable

A. Circle the letter of the best meaning for each vocabulary word.

1. fray: a) praise b) frazzle c) race d) demand
2. inalienable: a) forfeitable b) unimpeachable c) separated d) eccentric
3. cower: a) discover b) protest c) cringe d) hasten
4. gloat: a) exult b) defend c) argue d) simplify
5. inalienable: a) lost b) unforfeitable c) immigrant d) not spoken
6. frayed: a) mended b) forfeited c) tattered d) braced

B. Supply the proper form of the most appropriate vocabulary word.

1. The king's claim to the throne was ________________; there was no danger of his having to forfeit his position.
2. The American system of justice holds that the accused's right to a defense is ________________ and cannot be denied for any reason.
3. After six years of wear, the sleeves of the coat were completely ________________.
4. Freedom of expression is a(n) ________________ right that is dear to most Americans.
5. The vagrant was slovenly dressed in dirty pants, worn shoes, and a(n) ________________ jacket.

Lesson 65

chide (v) (chīd)

ORIGIN: Old English *cidan* (quarrel or strife)
MEANING: To scold, to find fault with, or to express disapproval of
CONTEXT: "Mother *chided* the children for disturbing Grandfather with their noisy games."
SYNONYMS: reprove, rebuke, scold, reprimand
ANTONYM: praise

insurgent (n) (in-'sər-jənt)

ORIGIN: Latin *insurgens* (rising up against)
MEANING: One who rises in opposition or revolt, especially against lawful authority, methods, or policies
CONTEXT: "The *insurgents* were rounded up by the army on the eve of the rebellion."
SYNONYMS: revolutionary, rebel, mutineer
OTHER FORMS: insurgent (adj.), insurgence (n.), insurgency (n.)

A. Circle the letter of the word that best completes each analogy.

1. genial: agreeable : : _______: sacred
   a) inalienable b) insurgent c) rational d) staunch
2. reprimand: reward : : _______: praise
   a) chide b) squall c) fray d) revoke
3. listless: animated : : _______: sensible
   a) rational b) inalienable c) irrational d) insurgent

B. Supply the proper form of the most appropriate vocabulary word.

1. When the revolt was finally put down, the government punished the ________________ severely.
2. Mr. Robinson ________________ the workers so harshly for their simple mistake that they decided to quit.
3. Joseph Cinqué led the ________________ of a group of slaves aboard the slave ship *Amistad.*
4. Although Thomas Jefferson stated that liberty is a(n) ________________ right of all men, he was, nevertheless, a slaveholder.
5. "Don't ________________ her," retorted Karen, tired of seeing her younger sister continually scolded for the misbehavior of other children.

Lesson 66

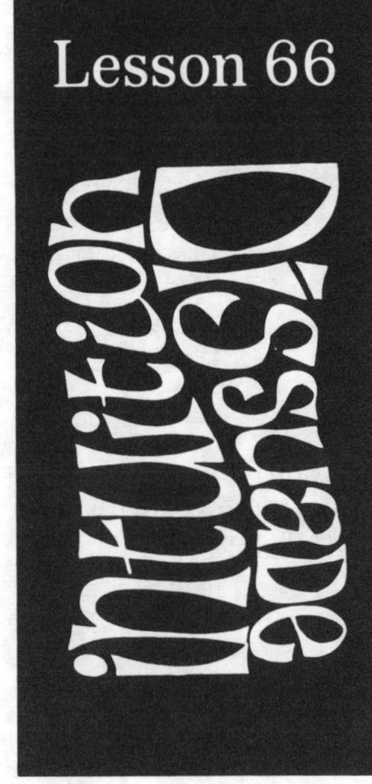

dissuade (v) (dis-'wād)

ORIGIN: Latin *dissuad* (to persuade)
MEANING: To persuade not to do something
CONTEXT: "Father tried hard to *dissuade* Will from leaving school to volunteer for the Marine Corps, but Will went anyway."
SYNONYMS: discourage, divert, restrain, remonstrate
ANTONYM: urge
OTHER FORMS: dissuasion (n.), dissuasive (adj.)

intuition (n) (,in-t[y]u-'ish-ən)

ORIGIN: Latin *intuitus* (to look at, to contemplate)
MEANING: The power of knowing immediately and without conscious reasoning
CONTEXT: "My *intuition* told me to say nothing of Father's illness to the family until I heard from the doctor again."
SYNONYM: insight
OTHER FORMS: intuitive (adj.), intuitively (adv.)

A. Circle the letter of the word that best completes each analogy.

1. equivocal: ambiguous : : ______: insightful
   a) staunch b) intuitive c) listless d) amorous
2. consummate: perfect : : ______: discourage
   a) bequeath b) fray c) dissuade d) connive
3. buttress: reinforcement : : ______: insight
   a) rostrum b) effigy c) stipulation d) intuition
4. gloat: exult : : ______: scold
   a) squall b) revoke c) nurture d) chide

B. Supply the proper form of the most appropriate vocabulary word.

1. When Walter smiled at Betsy in the hall between classes, her ______________ told her that he was going to ask for help with the science homework.
2. Mr. Andrews ______________ Lara for her disrespectful remark.
3. The ______________ force led by Che Guevara failed to overthrow the government.
4. "I want to go, and you can't ______________ me," Polly asserted firmly.
5. Ms. Morgan left the reception early because she felt ______________ that something had gone wrong at home.

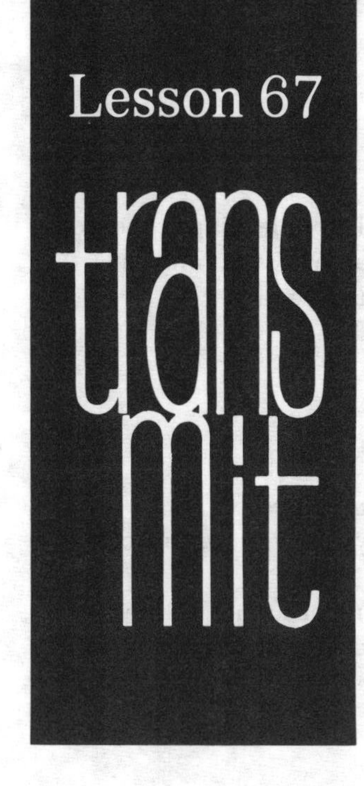

trans- (prefix)

ORIGIN: Latin *trans* (through)
MEANING: Across, beyond, through, over
CONTEXT: "*trans*port"

-mit- (root)

ORIGIN: Latin *mittere* (to send)
MEANING: To send out
CONTEXT: "trans*mit*"
OTHER FORMS: -mitt- (inter*mitt*ent), -miss- (trans*miss*ion)
NOTE: Do not confuse the variant form of *-mit-* (*-miss-*) with the prefix *mis-*, which means "wrong" or "bad."

A. In each of the italicized words below, underline the word parts that you have learned. Then, using your knowledge of the meanings of the word parts, circle the letter of the best meaning for the italicized word. (For some words there may be only one word part.)

1. *transmigration* of the soul: a) sacredness b) movement from one body to another c) simplicity d) sensitivity to what is not visible
2. presidential *missive:* a) letter b) privilege c) error d) office
3. *remit* money: a) cash b) save c) send back d) purchase
4. *transgress* on private property: a) invest in b) add to c) cross boundaries of d) send settlers into
5. *emit* a signal: a) receive b) detect c) send out d) screen
6. *incongruous* conduct: a) not suitable b) hypothetical c) established in advance d) abundant
7. struck by a *missile:* a) thrown object b) new idea c) obvious error d) enemy

B. REVIEW: Write one sentence for each of the following words. Each sentence must be complete enough to indicate the meaning of the vocabulary word through context clues and must not simply be an adaptation of a sentence in this book.

1. cower 2. intuition 3. chide 4. squall 5. insurgent
6. larceny 7. alien 8. fray 9. dissuade 10. rational

Lesson 68

appall (v) (ə-ˈpȯl)

ORIGIN: Middle French *apalir* (grow or make pale)
MEANING: To overcome or fill with dismay, consternation, fear, or horror
CONTEXT: "The amount of damage that resulted from last week's hurricane *appalled* us."
SYNONYMS: horrify, daunt, dismay, petrify
ANTONYM: embolden
OTHER FORM: appalling (adj.)

transition (n) (trans[t]s-ˈish-ən)

ORIGIN: Latin *transition* (a going across)
MEANING: A going from one position, stage, concept, place, or state to another
CONTEXT: "Some youths make the *transition* from high school to college quite easily, while others find the change extremely difficult."
SYNONYMS: change, shift

A. Circle the letter of the best meaning for each vocabulary word.

1. appall: a) carry b) appear c) dismay d) punish
2. transition: a) electronic tube b) message c) change d) forgetfulness
3. appalling: a) horrifying b) simple c) aesthetic d) unnecessary
4. endorse: a) cash b) support c) finish d) clarify
5. transitional: a) conventional b) shifting c) additional d) quick

B. Supply the proper form of the most appropriate vocabulary word.

1. The ________________ from public to private ownership of the postal service was so smooth that the average citizen was unaware of the change.
2. Handing back our first set of themes, the teacher remarked that the large number of spelling errors in the themes was ________________.
3. Although the volunteers' plan to sabotage the enemy's supply depot was extremely dangerous, they could not be ________________ from attempting it.
4. Expressions such as "in addition" and "however" help to signal a(n) ________________ from one idea to another in an essay.
5. The carelessness of the workers on the assembly line ________________ the newly hired supervisor.

saga (n) ('sȧg-ə)

ORIGIN: Icelandic *saga* (say)
MEANING: Any narrative or legend of heroic exploits
CONTEXT: "The children in the sixth grade class especially enjoyed the *saga* of Harriet Tubman."
SYNONYMS: epic, tale

negligible (adj) ('neg-li-jə-bəl)

ORIGIN: Latin *neglegere* (slight)
MEANING: Being so small or unimportant that it may be disregarded or neglected
CONTEXT: "You do not need to report those *negligible* expenses."
SYNONYM: trifling
ANTONYMS: important, central
OTHER FORMS: negligibility (n.), negligibly (adv.), negligence (n. meaning "carelessness"), negligent (adj.)

A. Circle the letter of the best meaning for each vocabulary word.

1. saga: a) sagginess b) hero c) tale d) deception
2. negligence: a) insolence b) care c) carelessness d) weakness
3. saga: a) epic b) error c) element d) eagerness
4. appall: a) confuse b) argue c) horrify d) bungle
5. negligible: a) central b) trifling c) forgotten d) naked

B. Supply the proper form of the most appropriate vocabulary word.

1. The ________________ of the Japanese samurai are as exciting as the tales of the American West but are almost totally unknown to the average American reader.
2. Since the difference between the two classes was ________________, it did not matter which one the new student joined.
3. Mike's slovenly appearance ________________ his fastidious aunt.
4. The workers' unwillingness to support the new management made the ________________ extremely difficult.
5. Since the experiment revealed that the amount of magnesium in the sample was ________________, we decided to ignore it in calculating the results.
6. The ________________ of the pioneers has always been a popular fireside tale.

Lesson 70

oscillate (v) ('äs-ə-,lāt)

ORIGIN: Latin *oscillatus* (swung)
MEANING: To swing or move to and fro
CONTEXT: "Peter *oscillates* daily between great happiness and deep despair."
SYNONYMS: swing, vary, fluctuate, vibrate, waver
ANTONYM: steady
OTHER FORM: oscillation (n.)

contingent (adj) (kən-'tin-jənt)

ORIGIN: Latin *contingens* (have contact with)
MEANING: Dependent for character, existence, or happening on something that is not yet certain
CONTEXT: "Our plans for the holidays are *contingent* on whether or not Cynthia has an exam shortly after we would return."
SYNONYMS: conditional, possible, provisional, subject to
OTHER FORMS: contingency (n.), contingently (adv.)

A. Circle the letter of the best meaning for each vocabulary word.

1. oscillate: a) scold b) return c) fluctuate d) expect
2. saga: a) name b) tale c) hallucination d) hatred
3. contingent: a) metallic b) important c) provisional d) coerced
4. contingency; a) volume b) stringency c) possibility d) exhilaration
5. oscillation: a) happiness b) nurturance c) vibration d) quality

B. Supply the proper form of the most appropriate vocabulary word.

1. Class participation often ________________ from full involvement to apathy, depending on the mood of the students.
2. The children enjoyed hearing the ________________ of their parents' dog-sled trek across Alaska.
3. "Whether or not you go out tonight is ________________ on whether Dad decides to punish you for being rude to our guests last night," Mother informed Jonathan.
4. Knowing that his election was ________________ on impressing the public, the candidate was very genial and cooperative while on speaking tours.
5. "Since your work has improved only ________________ since my last note, I am going to send another warning home to your parents," Al's science teacher told him.

-scrib- (root)

ORIGIN: Latin *scribere* (to write)
MEANING: To write
CONTEXT: "in*scribe*"
OTHER FORM: -script- (*script*ures)

-graph- (root)

ORIGIN: Greek *graphein* (to write)
MEANING: To write
CONTEXT: "auto*graph*"
OTHER FORM: -gram- (tele*gram*)

A. In each of the italicized words below, underline the word part that you have learned. Then, using your knowledge of the meaning of the word part, circle the letter of the best meaning for the italicized word.

1. completed *manuscript:* a) betrayal b) maneuver c) written text d) lecture
2. puzzling *cryptogram:* a) dialogue b) message in code c) position in an argument d) thought process
3. concise *telegram:* a) diagnosis b) joke c) written communication d) command
4. *proscribe* use of dangerous drugs: a) read about b) learn about c) hope for d) write a prohibition against
5. witty *epigram:* a) comedian b) comedienne c) short poem d) visitor
6. aesthetic *photography:* a) flower arranging b) taste c) etched images d) ideas
7. religious *scripture:* a) tithing b) class c) writings d) belief
8. diligent *scribe:* a) teacher b) prisoner c) writer d) apprentice

B. REVIEW: Write one sentence for each of the following words. Each sentence must be complete enough to indicate the meaning of the vocabulary word through context clues and must not simply be an adaptation of a sentence in this book.

1. contingent 2. condolence 3. oscillate 4. saga 5. fray
6. rostrum 7. negligible 8. transition 9. bane 10. appall

Lesson 72

forestall (v) (fōr-ʹstȯl)

ORIGIN: Middle English *forstalle* (intervention)
MEANING: To hinder or prevent by measures taken in advance
CONTEXT: "The school principal *forestalled* a lot of trouble on Halloween by allowing the young people to have a costume party in the gym."
SYNONYMS: prevent, obstruct, deter, inhibit
ANTONYM: facilitate
OTHER FORM: forestallment (n.)

skeptical (adj) (ʹskep-ti-kəl)

ORIGIN: Greek *skeptikos* (thoughtful, inquiring)
MEANING: Questioning; having or showing doubt
CONTEXT: "Because you question everything the teacher says, I think you are either quite *skeptical* or simply hardheaded."
SYNONYMS: doubtful, unbelieving, uncertain
ANTONYMS: confident, convinced
OTHER FORMS: skeptically (adv.), skeptic (n.), skepticism (n.)

A. Circle the letter of the best meaning for each vocabulary word.

1. forestall: a) seat b) prevent c) facilitate d) forego
2. skeptical: a) blind b) doubtful c) deprived d) unhappy
3. forestallment: a) endowment b) payment c) prevention d) endorsement
4. oscillate: a) transform b) swing c) question d) radiate
5. skepticism: a) miracle b) thought c) honesty d) uncertainty
6. contingent: a) desperate b) competitive c) dependent d) doubtful

B. Supply the proper form of the most appropriate vocabulary word.

1. Uncertain about the wisdom of the policy, the ________________ senator proposed an alternate plan.
2. "No matter how you try to prevent the court martial, nothing can ________________ it now," Captain Blake told the defense lawyer.
3. The ________________ amount of gold found in the foothills disappointed the people who had invested in the mining venture.
4. "Let me try to ________________ him," Edna proposed. "I may be able to convince him to wait a bit."
5. When it comes to ESP and other strange phenomena, I am quite a(n) ________________.

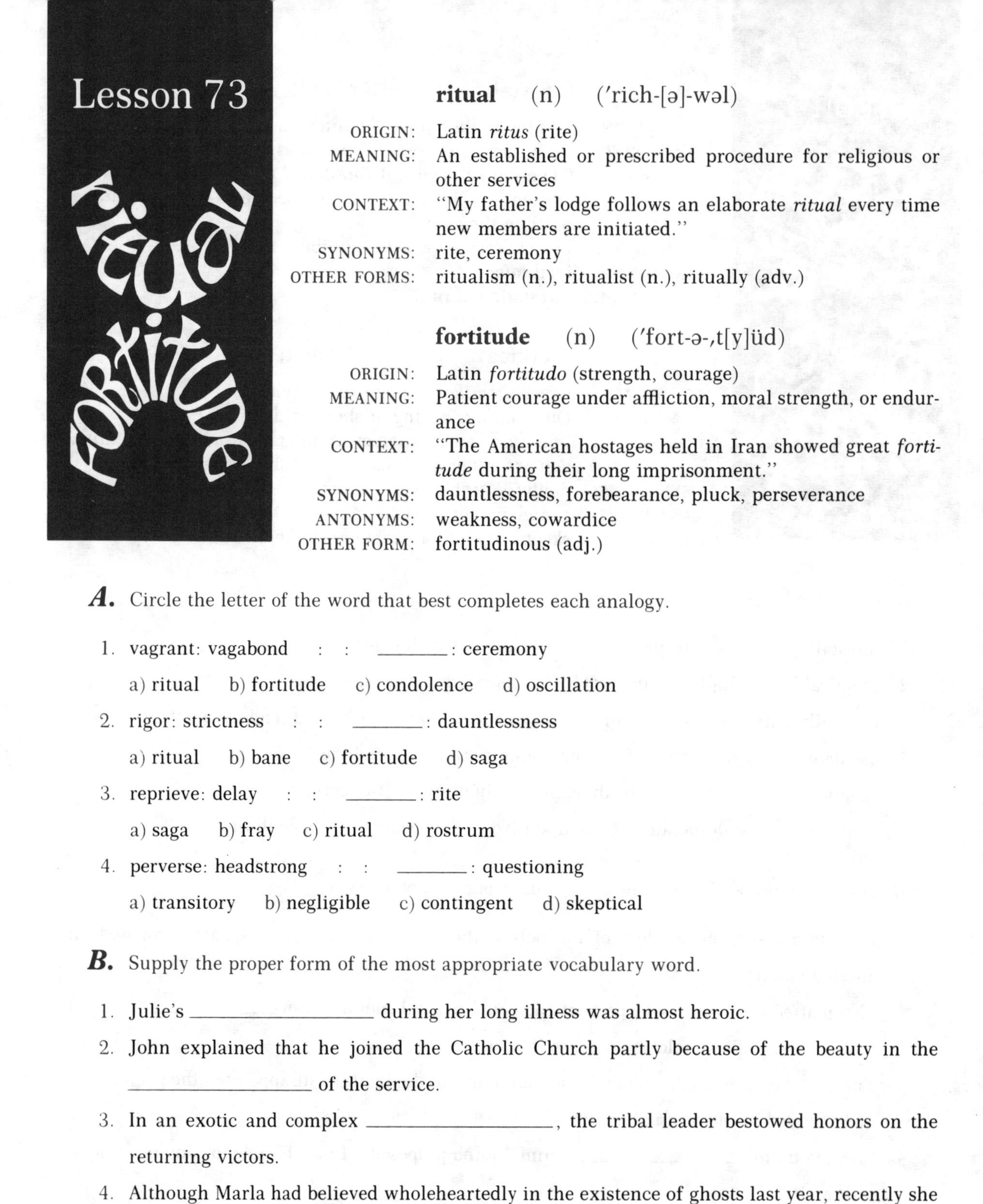

Lesson 73

ritual (n) ('rich-[ə]-wəl)

ORIGIN: Latin *ritus* (rite)
MEANING: An established or prescribed procedure for religious or other services
CONTEXT: "My father's lodge follows an elaborate *ritual* every time new members are initiated."
SYNONYMS: rite, ceremony
OTHER FORMS: ritualism (n.), ritualist (n.), ritually (adv.)

fortitude (n) ('fort-ə-,t[y]üd)

ORIGIN: Latin *fortitudo* (strength, courage)
MEANING: Patient courage under affliction, moral strength, or endurance
CONTEXT: "The American hostages held in Iran showed great *fortitude* during their long imprisonment."
SYNONYMS: dauntlessness, forebearance, pluck, perseverance
ANTONYMS: weakness, cowardice
OTHER FORM: fortitudinous (adj.)

A. Circle the letter of the word that best completes each analogy.

1. vagrant: vagabond : : ________: ceremony
   a) ritual b) fortitude c) condolence d) oscillation
2. rigor: strictness : : ________: dauntlessness
   a) ritual b) bane c) fortitude d) saga
3. reprieve: delay : : ________: rite
   a) saga b) fray c) ritual d) rostrum
4. perverse: headstrong : : ________: questioning
   a) transitory b) negligible c) contingent d) skeptical

B. Supply the proper form of the most appropriate vocabulary word.

1. Julie's ____________________ during her long illness was almost heroic.
2. John explained that he joined the Catholic Church partly because of the beauty in the ____________________ of the service.
3. In an exotic and complex ____________________, the tribal leader bestowed honors on the returning victors.
4. Although Marla had believed wholeheartedly in the existence of ghosts last year, recently she has shown signs of ____________________.

vantage (n) ('vant-ij)

ORIGIN: Middle French *avantage* (advantage)
MEANING: A place, condition, or position that affords some advantage or superiority
CONTEXT: "Unable to see the performers because of the huge crowd, we found a *vantage* atop an abandoned ladder."
SYNONYMS: advantage, benefit, leverage
ANTONYM: disadvantage

sedate (adj) (si-'dāt)

ORIGIN: Latin *sedare* (to allay, quiet)
MEANING: Keeping a quiet, steady attitude or pace; unruffled
CONTEXT: "I remember Joe as a high-strung, uncontrolled youngster; now he is a *sedate* young man."
SYNONYMS: staid, serene, unperturbed, tranquil, serious
ANTONYMS: excited, nervous
OTHER FORMS: sedately (adv.), sedateness (n.), sedative (n.)

A. Circle the letter of the best meaning for each vocabulary word.

1. vantage: a) attitude b) ventilation c) sale d) position of superiority
2. ritual: a) correction b) ceremony c) repertoire d) gift
3. sedate: a) calm b) sensitive c) scornful d) surpassed
4. vantage: a) walkway b) advantage c) uncertainty d) affection
5. sedately: a) excitedly b) sarcastically c) serenely d) honestly

B. Supply the proper form of the most appropriate vocabulary word.

1. "From my ________________ on the school board, I can easily predict your promotion to principal," Ms. Swanson told the candidate.
2. The commencement procession moved ________________ across the quadrangle and passed slowly through the Gothic entrance to the auditorium.
3. Her position as debating coach gave Mrs. Dickson a(n) ________________ from which to observe which students were good public speakers.
4. Many braves became "blood brothers" by performing the ancient ________________ of cutting their arms and mixing their blood.
5. In their trek west, many pioneer women demonstrated great ________________ against terrible odds.

Lesson 75

transcend (v) (tran[t]s-'end)

ORIGIN: Latin *transcendere* (to surmount)
MEANING: To exceed, rise above, or go beyond the limits of; to outdo or surpass
CONTEXT: "During Tim's great misfortune, the kindness of the townspeople *transcended* mere courtesy."
SYNONYMS: outstrip, excel, eclipse
OTHER FORMS: transcendingly (adv.), transcendent (adj.)

concoct (v) (kən-'käkt)

ORIGIN: Latin *concoquire* (to cook together)
MEANING: To make up, to devise, to prepare by combining a number of ingredients
CONTEXT: "Some students spend their time *concocting* schemes by which to avoid doing any work."
SYNONYMS: fabricate, invent, contrive, plan
OTHER FORM: concoction (n.)

A. Circle the letter of the best meaning for each vocabulary word.

1. concoct: a) drink b) invent c) tease d) signal
2. concoction: a) preparation b) question c) conclusion d) sculpture
3. transcend: a) transact b) excel c) forbid d) transgress
4. sedate: a) tall b) serious c) solid d) tiny
5. vantage: a) small footbridge b) ramp c) superior position d) bequest
6. transcendent: a) scornful b) surpassing c) quick d) false

B. Supply the proper form of the most appropriate vocabulary word.

1. Collecting all the leftover foods in the refrigerator, William quickly ______________ an unusual and tasty stew.
2. Lois's imaginative design for a shopping center ______________ the more commonplace work produced by other first-year architectural students.
3. Living in England for a year gave Inez a(n) ______________ from which to view American culture objectively.
4. The warlocks' brew was a magical ______________ devised to conjure up the spirits of the dead.
5. The rugged beauty of the Rockies near Estes Park ______________ all description.

Lesson 76

-ten- (root)

ORIGIN: Latin *tenere* (to have or hold)
MEANING: To hold, contain
CONTEXT: "*ten*acious"
OTHER FORMS: -tin- (con*tin*ent), -tent- (con*tent*), -tain- (re*tain*)

-sta- (root)

ORIGIN: Latin *stare* (to stand)
MEANING: To stand
CONTEXT: "in*sta*nce"
OTHER FORMS: -stat- (*stat*us), -sist- (re*sist*), -sti- (sub*sti*tute)

A. In each of the italicized words below, underline the word parts that you have learned. Then, using your knowledge of the meanings of the word parts, circle the letter of the best meaning for the italicized word. (For some words there may be only one word part.)

1. the deadly *tentacles:* a) poisons b) sea animals c) grasping appendages d) wounds
2. a *stable* barometer: a) expensive b) weather c) unmoving d) fluctuating
3. church *tenet:* a) tithe b) assistant minister c) doctrine held to be true d) pulpit
4. *established* in the faith: a) created b) not to be found c) fixed d) remiss
5. *scribble* notes: a) write hastily b) discover c) rip up d) dictate
6. *attain* a goal: a) dream of b) talk about c) forget d) take hold of
7. *constitutes* justice: a) prevents b) stands for c) denies d) hastens
8. a *static* character: a) changeable b) argumentative c) unchanging d) literary
9. *continent* behavior: a) free enough b) needed c) able to hold back d) rebellious
10. well-spoken *missionary:* a) one who writes books b) one who is sent to preach c) one who collects art treasures d) one who studies tribal customs

B. REVIEW: Write one sentence for each of the following words. Each sentence must be complete enough to indicate the meaning of the vocabulary word through context clues and must not simply be an adaptation of a sentence in this book.

1. concoct 2. intuition 3. sedate 4. gad 5. vantage
6. transcend 7. ritual 8. forestall 9. oscillate 10. dissuade

Lesson 77

auspices (n) (ʹȯ-spə-səz)

ORIGIN: Latin *avis* (bird) + *specere* (to look at)
MEANING: Kindly patronage, sponsorship, support
CONTEXT: "The program was brought to the campus under the *auspices* of the fine arts department."
SYNONYMS: protection, supervision, influence, charge, care, support
OTHER FORM: auspicious (adj. meaning "favorable")

fervent (adj) (ʹfər-vənt)

ORIGIN: Latin *fervere* (to boil)
MEANING: Having or showing great intensity of spirit
CONTEXT: "Having suffered at the hands of prejudiced people himself, the speaker was able to make a *fervent* plea for more tolerance toward minority groups."
SYNONYMS: ardent, zealous, impassioned, enthusiastic
ANTONYMS: apathetic, listless
OTHER FORMS: fervently (adv.), fervor (n.), fervid (adj.)

A. Circle the letter of the best meaning for each vocabulary word.

1. auspices: a) prophecy b) happiness c) sponsorship d) allowance
2. fervent: a) ardent b) ill c) protected d) narrow-minded
3. auspicious: a) birdlike b) favorable c) small d) strong
4. fervor: a) listlessness b) coloring c) enthusiasm d) decay
5. vantage: a) advantage b) vault c) guard d) hill
6. forestall: a) prevent b) encourage c) generalize d) foresee

B. Supply the proper form of the most appropriate vocabulary word.

1. We decided that the charity drive would be held under the ________________ of the local group rather than the national organization.
2. ________________ pleas for aid for the drought-stricken country were broadcast daily.
3. "The battle is not going too well for us," the general observed from his ________________ point on a hill overlooking the besieged plain.
4. The thunderous applause that greeted the opening number convinced us that our variety show had gotten off to a(n) ________________ start.
5. Since only a(n) *(trifling)* ________________ amount of snow fell last night, the roads were dry by 10 A.M.

Lesson 78

grotesque (adj) (grō-'tesk)

ORIGIN: Italian *pittura grottesca* (cave painting)
MEANING: Fantastically absurd, ugly, or unnatural in shape, appearance, or character
CONTEXT: "To me there is nothing pleasing about that vase because of the *grotesque* decoration on it."
SYNONYMS: misshapen, unsightly, repulsive, abhorrent
ANTONYMS: customary, normal, aesthetic
OTHER FORMS: grotesqueness (n.), grotesquely (adv.)

adamant (adj) ('ad-ə-mənt)

ORIGIN: Latin *adamas* (hardest metal)
MEANING: Utterly unyielding in substance or attitude
CONTEXT: "He remained *adamant* in his decision to resign in spite of the pleading of his friends."
SYNONYMS: inflexible, firm, unyielding, implacable, solid
ANTONYMS: flexible, yielding
OTHER FORM: adamantly (adv.)

A. Circle the letter of the best meaning for each vocabulary word.

1. grotesque: a) angry b) enormous c) misshapen d) neglectful
2. adamant: a) confessed b) flexible c) unyielding d) additional
3. auspices: a) luck b) sponsorship c) austerity d) solidity
4. adamant: a) firm b) coarse c) unpredictable d) sold
5. fervent: a) deathly sick b) impassioned c) crowded d) earned

B. Supply the proper form of the most appropriate vocabulary word.

1. As the debate dragged on, we could see that Phyllis was becoming more and more ______________ in her refusal to see the other side of the issue.
2. The controversial Picasso sculpture in Chicago is thought by some people to be a(n) ______________ eyesore, while others find its beauty overwhelming.
3. The ______________ of the Halloween costume frightened the small child.
4. Bright, sunny weather signaled a(n) ______________ beginning for our trip.
5. The ______________ with which Senator Cartwright denounced the increase in federal spending caused the audience to cheer loudly.
6. Unaffected by her father's request that she stay home, Carol was ______________ about going on the ski trip.

Lesson 79

farce (n) (fȧrs)

ORIGIN: Latin *farsus* (stuffed)
MEANING: A foolish show; a ridiculous sham; mockery
CONTEXT: "'To assume that all people will stop smoking because it is dangerous to their health is a *farce,*' declared the speaker."
SYNONYMS: absurdity, nonsense, travesty, pretense, untruth
ANTONYM: truth
OTHER FORM: farcical (adj.)

accost (v) (ə-ˈkȯst)

ORIGIN: Latin *accostare* (to be put side by side)
MEANING: To approach or confront boldly
CONTEXT: "The police *accosted* the old woman outside her home and demanded to see her identification."
SYNONYMS: address, face
ANTONYM: avoid

A. Circle the letter of the word that best completes each analogy.

1. vantage: benefit : : ________: absurdity
   a) farce b) grotesqueness c) fervor d) auspices
2. oscillate: vibrate : : ________: confront
   a) gad b) chide c) accost d) concoct
3. aesthetic: beautiful : : ________: ugly
   a) farce b) vantage c) grotesque d) ritual
4. skeptical: questioning : : ________: unyielding
   a) intuitive b) adamant c) sedate d) fervent

B. Supply the proper form of the most appropriate vocabulary word.

1. Since Ed never meant to keep his word, his promise was a(n) ________________.
2. The vagrant ________________ shoppers outside the large department store, badgering them for quarters.
3. The FBI ________________ the strangers as they left the hotel and questioned them about their mysterious activities.
4. The nonsensical pantomime was a(n) ________________.
5. From the firmness in her voice, Greg knew Liz was ________________ in her position.

Lesson 80

craven innovation

craven (adj) ('krā-vən)

ORIGIN: Middle English *cravant* (overthrown)
MEANING: Contemptibly timid, cowardly
CONTEXT: "It was a *craven* act on the part of the young boys to run from the scene of the accident."
SYNONYMS: defeated, dastardly, timorous, cowering
ANTONYMS: fearless, intrepid, bold, fortitudinous
OTHER FORMS: cravenly (adv.), cravenness (n.)

innovation (n) (,in-ə-'vā-shən)

ORIGIN: Latin *innovatus* (renewed, altered) + *ion* (action)
MEANING: Something new or different introduced
CONTEXT: "A radical *innovation* in the English department curriculum encouraged both students and teachers to become more creative."
SYNONYMS: novelty, introduction
ANTONYMS: tradition, custom
OTHER FORMS: innovate (v.), innovative (adj.), innovator (n.)

A. Circle the letter of the word that best completes each analogy.

1. transcend: excel : : ________: introduce
   a) surpass b) surmise c) nurture d) innovate
2. declare: intimate : : ________: avoid
   a) exhilarate b) condone c) sympathize d) accost
3. vehement: fervent : : ________: cowering
   a) illegal b) destroyed c) craven d) swearing

B. Supply the proper form of the most appropriate vocabulary word.

1. After spending an entire year researching new methods of teaching, the faculty committee proposed a very ____________________ curriculum.
2. The angry owner ____________________ the other driver after discovering the dented car fender.
3. The man hung back ____________________ when he saw the gang of toughs approaching.
4. Since the mayor consistently upheld measures to raise taxes, the townspeople felt her campaign promises to lower taxes were a(n) ____________________.
5. The more traditional stockholders vetoed plans to introduce ____________________ in production methods at the factory.

Lesson 81

de- (prefix)

ORIGIN: Latin *de* (from, down, away)
MEANING 1: down
CONTEXT 1: "*de*press"
MEANING 2: away
CONTEXT 2: "*de*part"
MEANING 3: reversing or undoing action
CONTEXT 3: "*de*populate"

epi- (prefix)

ORIGIN: Greek *epi* (on, upon, to)
MEANING: Upon, above, over, outside
CONTEXT: "*epi*dermis"

A. In each of the italicized words below, underline the word parts that you have learned. Then, using your knowledge of the meanings of the word parts, choose the correct meaning for the italicized word. (For some words there may be only one word part.)

1. *descend* the mountain: a) explore b) photograph c) go down d) bypass
2. the *epidermal* tissue: a) internal b) healing c) soft d) outside
3. *deactivate* the bomb: a) jiggle b) explode c) examine d) undo its harmfulness
4. solemn *epitaph:* a) procession through a forest b) speech c) inscription on a tombstone d) oath taken before dying
5. *transpose* the music: a) play b) listen to c) put it over into another key d) write
6. *desist* action: a) start over b) "stare away"; that is, ignore c) "stand down"; that is, stop d) "fold over"; that is, involve
7. an *immutable* element: a) expensive b) rare c) unchanging d) radioactive
8. the *epicenter* of the quake: a) result b) under the exact center c) place on earth's surface above center of earthquake d) cause

B. REVIEW: Write one sentence for each of the following words. Each sentence must be complete enough to indicate the meaning of the vocabulary word through context clues and must not simply be an adaptation of a sentence in this book.

1. innovation 2. sedate 3. craven 4. auspices 5. fervent
6. accost 7. fortitude 8. adamant 9. skeptical 10. grotesque

Lesson 82

derange (v) (di-'rānj)

ORIGIN: Latin *de* (from) + *reng* (place)
MEANING: To throw into disorder; to make insane
CONTEXT: "The arrival of the unexpected guest *deranged* our whole evening."
SYNONYMS: unbalance, disturb, dement, confuse, disorganize
ANTONYM: order
OTHER FORMS: derangement (n.), deranged (adj.)

vulnerable (adj) ('vəln-[ə]-rə-bəl)

ORIGIN: Latin *vulnerare* (to wound)
MEANING: Capable of being wounded or hurt; open to attack or to criticism
CONTEXT: "The bridge is *vulnerable* to attack by the enemy from two directions."
SYNONYMS: exposed, accessible, unprotected, assailable
ANTONYM: protected
OTHER FORMS: vulnerableness (n.), vulnerability (n.)

A. Circle the letter of the best meaning of each vocabulary word.

1. derange: a) debate b) devote c) disturb d) act
2. craven: a) black b) frightening c) accidental d) timorous
3. vulnerable: a) violent b) depressed c) exposed d) vengeful
4. deranged: a) orderly b) disturbed c) purified d) guilty
5. innovation: a) exchange b) bequest c) novelty d) accusation
6. vulnerability: a) auspices b) propriety c) openness to harm d) kindness

B. Supply the proper form of the most appropriate vocabulary word.

1. Consuming too much alcohol can ________________ the normal functioning of the kidneys.
2. The reason that so many of us rarely talk frankly about ourselves is that we do not want to be ________________ to criticism by others.
3. Achilles had only one ________________ spot on his body—the heel.
4. Having seen so many cases of tax fraud, Jill Danforth, the IRS representative, is often ________________ about the income tax forms she audits.
5. Living alone in the eerie, old house ________________ the old hermit's mind.

Lesson 83

decipher (v) (di-ˈsī-fər)

ORIGIN: Middle Latin *de* (from) + *cifra* (empty, zero)
MEANING: To make out the meaning of unclear writing, or to discover the meaning of something obscure
CONTEXT: "Because of poor and partially obliterated writing, several experts were required to *decipher* the old manuscript."
SYNONYMS: interpret, decode, translate
OTHER FORMS: decipherable (adj.), indecipherable (adj.), decipherability (n.), decipherment (n.)

girth (n) (gərth)

ORIGIN: Scandinavian *gjordh* (girdle, hoop)
MEANING: The measure around anything; the strap that goes around anything
CONTEXT: "The *girth* of the giant poplar was so great that the two of us together could not reach around it."
SYNONYMS: girdle, circumference, dimension, size

A. Circle the letter of the best meaning for each vocabulary word.

1. decipher: a) code b) deceive c) translate d) upset
2. girth: a) weight b) circumference c) volume d) height
3. decipherable: a) unclear b) discoverable c) unbearable d) guilty
4. vantage: a) vault b) advantage c) mistake d) vent
5. derange: a) disturb b) imitate c) result d) belittle
6. girth: a) excitement b) temper c) dimension d) foolery

B. Supply the proper form of the most appropriate vocabulary word.

1. The cowboy fell off the bronco when the ________________ of his saddle broke.
2. Although it was transmitted in code, Captain Bailey could easily ________________ the message.
3. The ________________ man was committed to a mental hospital.
4. Still weak after the long illness, Inez was ________________ to even the slightest draft or infection.
5. The leather ________________ was fastened securely around the donkey's middle.
6. Teachers often resent having to ________________ my illegible handwriting.

Lesson 84

gist (n) (jist)

ORIGIN: Latin *jacere* (to lie)
MEANING: The main or essential part
CONTEXT: "Although the telephone connection was poor, I got the *gist* of what they had to say."
SYNONYMS: essence, point, substance
ANTONYM: irrelevance

converge (v) (kən-ˈvərj)

ORIGIN: Late Latin *converg* (incline together)
MEANING: To incline toward each other
CONTEXT: "The two highways *converge* just beyond the city limits."
SYNONYMS: near, approach, merge, join, focus
ANTONYMS: scatter, diverge
OTHER FORMS: convergence (n.), convergent (adj.)

A. Circle the letter of the word that best completes each analogy.

1. condone: excuse : : _______: merge

   a) transcend b) converge c) condole d) submerge

2. reprimand: censure : : _______: essence

   a) girth b) vantage c) gist d) saga

3. wrest: extract : : _______: excel

   a) remain b) transcend c) secrete d) integrate

4. diversity: variety : : _______: circumference

   a) context b) girth c) rostrum d) urbanity

B. Supply the proper form of the most appropriate vocabulary word.

1. Your notes should contain the ______________ of the lecture, not every detail.
2. Parallel lines are lines that do not ______________.
3. We fastened wire around the ______________ of the barrel to add strength.
4. Barb Findley, a dealer in herbs, mixed up a(n) *(preparation)* ______________ which she swore would cure colds, heart disease, and emotional problems.
5. A précis is a concise paragraph that summarizes the ______________ of an essay.
6. The defensive team's front line ______________ on the quarterback, forcing him to throw an interception.

-duct- (root)

ORIGIN: Latin *ducere* (to lead)
MEANING: To lead
CONTEXT: "in*duct*ion"
OTHER FORMS: -duce- (re*duce*), -ducat- (e*ducat*e)

dis- (prefix)

ORIGIN: Latin *dis* (apart)
MEANING 1: Not
CONTEXT 1: "*dis*honest"
MEANING 2: Apart from, away
CONTEXT 2: "*dis*connect"
OTHER FORMS: di- (*di*gress), dif- (*dif*fuse)

A. In each of the italicized words below, underline the word parts that you have learned. Then, using your knowledge of the meanings of the word parts, circle the letter of the best meaning for the italicized word. (For some words there may be only one part.)

1. *reduce* the temperature: a) "fold" it over b) "say" the amount c) "lead" it down d) "check" the intensity
2. *imperceptible* lines: a) entangle b) unable to be seen c) moving d) parallel
3. *induction* examination: a) unfinished b) entry c) difficult d) oral
4. *dispassionate* attitude: a) vehement b) not lively c) skeptical d) appalled
5. *involuted* wires: a) waterproofed b) taped c) twisted d) electrical
6. *ductile* metal: a) adamant b) advertised c) cold d) easily molded
7. *disseminate* pamphlets: a) turn down b) send out c) talk about d) tear up
8. *conducive* to change: a) lead to b) stand in the way of c) talk about d) oppose
9. *divert* traffic: a) control b) turn away c) send down an incline d) report on
10. *disrupt* routine: a) break away from b) talk against c) follow d) describe

B. REVIEW: Write one sentence for each of the following words. Each sentence must be complete enough to indicate the meaning of the vocabulary word through context clues and must not simply be an adaptation of a sentence in this book.

1. converge	2. accost	3. decipher	4. auspices	5. innovation
6. vulnerable	7. gist	8. craven	9. adamant	10. girth

Lesson 86

VIGIL DISRUPT

vigil (n) ('vij-əl)

ORIGIN: Middle Latin *vigilia* (eve of a holy day)
MEANING: A watch or a period of watchful attention
CONTEXT: "The mother kept a *vigil* at the bedside of her son until the doctor announced that he was out of danger."
SYNONYMS: surveillance, attention
ANTONYM: inattention
OTHER FORMS: vigilant (adj.), vigilante (n.), vigilance (n.)

disrupt (v) (dis-'rəpt)

ORIGIN: Latin *dirumpere* (to break)
MEANING: To cause disorder or turmoil, to break apart
CONTEXT: "The tornado *disrupted* all communication with neighboring areas for some time."
SYNONYMS: rupture, destroy, disorganize, interrupt, derange
ANTONYM: organize
OTHER FORMS: disruption (n.), disruptive (adj.)

A. Circle the letter of the best meaning for each vocabulary word.

1. vigil: a) virgin b) visit c) surveillance d) sedateness
2. vigilant: a) fastidious b) alert c) amorous d) temporary
3. chide: a) rebuke b) cherish c) endorse d) bungle
4. disrupt: a) deal with b) fool c) disorganize d) converge
5. decipher: a) hide b) escape c) entertain d) translate
6. disruptive: a) deceptive b) destructive c) determined d) teasing

B. Supply the proper form of the most appropriate vocabulary word.

1. Our conversation was __________________ by the chatter of Mrs. Lee's four-year-old son.
2. The guards kept a constant __________________ at their posts, watching closely for any sign of an intruder.
3. Bonnie's frequent trips to the pencil sharpener __________________ the work of other students in the study hall.
4. The Secretary of State explained the President's foreign policy in a(n) *(reasonable)* __________________ manner, so most citizens accepted it.
5. The __________________ of the private-duty nurse continued round the clock until his patient was out of danger.

Lesson 87

vex (v) (veks)

ORIGIN: Latin *vexare* (to shake, annoy)
MEANING: To torment, trouble, or irritate
CONTEXT: "Sally and Jeff found that the quickest way to *vex* Ms. Martin was to tap their pencils loudly and steadily on their desk tops."
SYNONYMS: anger, irk, nettle, harass, puzzle, annoy
ANTONYMS: delight, exhilarate
OTHER FORMS: vexation (n.), vexatious (adj.), vexingly (adv.)

dissect (v) (dis-′ekt)

ORIGIN: Latin *dissecare* (to cut up)
MEANING: To cut apart; to examine minutely part by part
CONTEXT: "Today the biology class will *dissect* frogs to examine their nervous system."
SYNONYMS: analyze, criticize, scrutinize, subdivide
ANTONYMS: integrate, consolidate
OTHER FORMS: dissectible (adj.), dissector (n.), dissection (n.)

A. Circle the letter of the word that is neither a synonym nor an antonym of the vocabulary word.

1. vex: a) puzzle b) exhilarate c) ignore d) irk
2. dissect: a) consolidate b) integrate c) subdivide d) destroy
3. vexation: a) delight b) annoyance c) harassment d) cleverness
4. vulnerable: a) hurt b) protected c) exposed d) assailable
5. dissection: a) criticism b) scrutiny c) medicine d) division
6. vigil: a) surveillance b) alertness c) inattention d) youthfulness

B. Supply the proper form of the most appropriate vocabulary word.

1. Kristin was ________________ when Juanita did not pick her up on time.
2. The lawyers ________________ the proposed contract, examining it clause by clause to be sure that their clients were fully protected.
3. The soldier who fell asleep on duty was punished severely for his lack of ________________.
4. When our new television did not work properly, my father was ________________.
5. Mr. Johnson told Donna her whispering was ________________ the class.
6. Our lab project in biology was to ________________ a cat.

Lesson 88

morality (n) (mə-'ral-ət-ē)

ORIGIN: Latin *moralis* (pertaining to usage, custom)
MEANING: Pertaining to or conforming to the rules of right conduct; virtue
CONTEXT: "Because their *morality* has never been questioned, I know we can depend on them to do what is just."
SYNONYMS: ethics, integrity, standards
ANTONYM: immorality
OTHER FORMS: moralist (n.), moral (adj.), moralize (v.)

immaculate (adj) (im-'ak-yə-lət)

ORIGIN: Latin *immaculat* (unspotted)
MEANING: Free from spot or stain; pure
CONTEXT: "Because many people living on Chicago's Gold Coast are wealthy enough to afford maids, their apartments are always *immaculate*."
SYNONYMS: spotless, taintless, stainless, flawless
ANTONYMS: squalid, filthy, impure
OTHER FORMS: immaculately (adv.), immaculateness (n.)

A. Circle the letter of the word that best completes each analogy.

1. surveillant: vigilant : : _______: divided
   a) adamant b) craven c) dissected d) immaculate
2. gloat: regret : : _______: delight
   a) innovate b) accost c) moralize d) vex
3. conglomerate: accumulated : : _______: subdivided
   a) immaculate b) dissected c) disruptive d) vulnerable

B. Supply the proper form of the most appropriate vocabulary word.

1. Many law schools now offer courses on ethics and ________________.
2. The nurse was dressed in a(n) ________________ white uniform and spotless white shoes.
3. The child's uncontrollable behavior ________________ the babysitter, who finally gave up and watched TV for the rest of the evening.
4. The evangelist preacher used her radio show to ________________ about the nature of good and evil.

pre- (prefix)

ORIGIN: Latin *prae* (before)
MEANING: Before, ahead of time, prior to, in front of
CONTEXT: "*pre*dict"
NOTE: You will also want to learn *post-*, a Latin prefix that means "after" or "later," as in *post*paid.

ante- (prefix)

ORIGIN: Latin *ante* (before, in front of)
MEANING: Prior to, before, in front of
CONTEXT: "*ante*cedent"
NOTE: Do not confuse *ante-* with *anti-*, a Greek prefix that means "against," as in *anti*aircraft.

A. In each of the italicized words below, underline the word parts that you have learned. Then, using your knowledge of the meanings of the word parts, circle the letter of the best meaning for the italicized word. (For some words there may be only one word part.)

1. *precursor* of the movement: a) newspaper b) forerunner c) results d) secrecy
2. *postpone* the party: a) R.S.V.P. b) make plans for c) put off until later d) "crash"
3. *antenuptial* plans: a) after the wedding b) before the wedding c) protesting the wedding d) in case of a wedding
4. logical *preamble:* a) position b) speaker c) introduction d) campaign
5. *antiwar* slogans: a) slogans in favor of the war b) slogans publicized before the war c) slogans aimed against the war d) slogans that are publicized widely
6. a *precognition:* a) conclusion b) idea ahead of time c) stomach ailment d) friend
7. large *anteroom:* a) powder room b) assembly hall c) back porch d) foyer
8. *anterior* section: a) forward b) last c) awkward d) darkened

B. **REVIEW:** Write one sentence for each of the following words. Each sentence must be complete enough to indicate the meaning of the vocabulary word through context clues and must not be simply an adaptation of a sentence in this book.

1. immaculate 2. vigil 3. morality 4. converge 5. adamant
6. dissect 7. vulnerable 8. sedate 9. vex 10. disrupt

Lesson 90

nestle (v) ('nes-əl)

ORIGIN: Old English *nestlian* (nestle)
MEANING: To settle snugly or comfortably
CONTEXT: "The child *nestled* her head on her mother's shoulder and fell asleep."
SYNONYMS: snuggle, cuddle, lodge, nuzzle

apparition (n) (ap-ə-'rish-ən)

ORIGIN: Latin *apparitio* (attendance)
MEANING: A ghost or phantom; the unexpected appearance of someone already dead
CONTEXT: "Marty claims to have seen an *apparition* that looked like her great-aunt Martha, who died on the *Titanic*."
SYNONYMS: specter, phantom, phenomenon, illusion, chimera, hallucination, ghost
OTHER FORM: apparitional (adj.)

A. Match each vocabulary word with its synonym by writing the proper letter in the blank.

1. apparitional ______ 2. moral ______ 3. apparition ______
4. nestle ______ 5. vigil ______ 6. immaculate ______

a) surveillance b) ghost c) snuggle d) ethical e) illusionary f) spotless

B. Supply the proper form of the most appropriate vocabulary word.

1. The newborn sparrows ________________ together for warmth.
2. The old Victorian mansion was said to be haunted by the ________________ of a woman who had mysteriously disappeared there.
3. To reduce the possibility of a patient's contracting an infection, the surgical suite in the hospital was kept ________________.
4. Some people think students in co-ed dorms have no sense of ________________.
5. The child wanted his night-light on because the fluttering white curtains in the shadowy room created frightening ________________.
6. While watching the late movie on television, Anita ________________ down into the sofa and was soon fast asleep.
7. The students presented a(n) ________________ argument to the principal, giving sensible reasons why students should have a much greater role in planning school affairs.

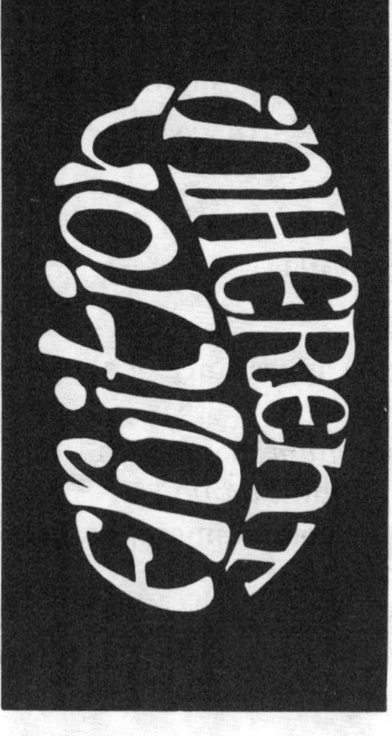

Lesson 91

inherent (adj) (in-ˈhir-ənt)

ORIGIN: Latin *inhaerent* (to adhere, to stick)
MEANING: Being a part of or belonging to the essential character of a person or thing
CONTEXT: "From earliest childhood, Ann has had an *inherent* sense of justice and fair play."
SYNONYMS: innate, intrinsic, inborn
ANTONYM: unnatural
OTHER FORMS: inherently (adv.), inherence (n.), inhere (v.)

fruition (n) (fru-ˈish-ən)

ORIGIN: Latin *fruitio* (enjoyment)
MEANING: Attainment of a goal
CONTEXT: "After long hours of difficult work, he brought his plans to *fruition*."
SYNONYMS: consummation, realization, completion
ANTONYM: failure

A. Circle the letters of the two words in each group that are most closely related in meaning.

1. a) learned b) heard c) inborn d) inherent
2. a) futility b) consummation c) fruition d) concoction
3. a) neglect b) nuzzle c) nestle d) muzzle
4. a) fulfillment b) fault c) fugitive d) fruition
5. a) witch doctor b) apparition c) phantom d) postulate
6. a) inherently b) noisily c) morally d) intrinsically

B. Supply the proper form of the most appropriate vocabulary word.

1. The instinct to survive is ________________ in all animals.
2. After toiling for years in the lab, the scientist's hopes came to ________________ when she discovered a new enzyme.
3. Deranged by a high fever, the elderly patient saw a(n) ________________ of Saint Peter.
4. Because attempts to bring negotiations to ________________ failed, the strike continued.
5. ________________ comfortably in the big leather chair, Margarita studied the maps.
6. Throughout history, frequent attempts have been made to prove the ________________ superiority of one race or nationality over another, but none has been valid or successful.

Lesson 92

GRIMACE DIVULGE

grimace (n) ('grim-əs)

ORIGIN: Old English *grima* (frown)
MEANING: A facial expression usually of disgust, disapproval, or pain
CONTEXT: "'Did you notice the *grimace* Jane made when her opponent was introduced?' whispered Mrs. Wilson."
SYNONYMS: frown, contortion
ANTONYM: smile
OTHER FORM: grimacingly (adv.)

divulge (v) (də-'vəlj)

ORIGIN: Latin *divulgare* (to make general or common)
MEANING: To make public, to disclose
CONTEXT: "The secretary *divulged* the content of the telegram even though it was confidential information."
SYNONYMS: reveal, tattle, impart, tell
ANTONYMS: conceal, hide
OTHER FORM: divulgence (n.)

A. Circle the letter of the word that best completes each analogy.

1. intimation: hint : : _______: consummation
   a) dissection b) fruition c) vexation d) vantage
2. fastidious: slovenly : : _______: unnatural
   a) contingent b) sedate c) adamant d) inherent
3. relinquish: procure : : _______: smile
   a) grimace b) vex c) nurture d) decipher
4. belittle: disparage : : _______: tattle
   a) divulge b) transcend c) oscillate d) gloat

B. Supply the proper form of the most appropriate vocabulary word.

1. Sworn to secrecy, the boy would not __________________ who broke the lamp.
2. Katie __________________ as she swallowed the distasteful cough medicine.
3. Her plan to sail across the Atlantic Ocean in a small boat never came to __________________.
4. __________________ of the club's secret password was grounds for expulsion.
5. Alan's __________________ ability to reason logically made trigonometry easy.
6. "Don't tell me this dress looks *that* bad!" exclaimed Mrs. Rossi when she saw the __________________ on her husband's face.

Lesson 93

entrench (v) (in-'trench)

ORIGIN: Latin *in* (cause to be) + Middle French *trenchier* (cut)
MEANING: To place in a position of strength; establish firmly
CONTEXT: "Mrs. Hardy has *entrenched* herself so firmly as head of the history department that replacing her will be hard."
SYNONYMS: establish, fortify
ANTONYMS: uproot, weaken
OTHER FORM: entrenchment (n.)

deficit (n) ('def-ə-sət)

ORIGIN: Latin *deficit* (it is wanting)
MEANING: A shortage in required amount
CONTEXT: "When the treasurer's books were audited, a considerable *deficit* was discovered."
SYNONYMS: lack, dearth
ANTONYMS: surplus, excess
OTHER FORMS: deficient (adj.), deficiency (n.)

A. Circle the letter of the word that best completes each analogy.

1. establish: eradicate : : _______: uproot
   a) entrench b) grimace c) nestle d) converge
2. stupor: listlessness : : _______: dearth
   a) fruition b) deficit c) moral d) vigil
3. chide: scold : : _______: frown
   a) vex b) divulge c) grimace d) entrench

B. Supply the proper form of the most appropriate vocabulary word.

1. An unexpected _________________ in the production funds forced us to cancel the play.
2. Sociologists describe families that have established themselves in a region and have intermarried frequently as being _________________.
3. When the _________________ in food supplies was discovered, panic ran rampant through the starving village.
4. When Josie decided to marry Randy, she _________________ her plans to no one, not even her best friend.
5. The bureaucrat was _________________ in old-fashioned procedures and could not be convinced that modern approaches were worth considering.

Lesson 94

fac fer

-fac- (root)

ORIGIN: Latin *facere* (to make or do)
MEANING: To make, to do
CONTEXT: "*fac*ulty"
OTHER FORMS: -fact- (manu*fact*ure), -fect- (per*fect*), -fic- (ef*fic*acious), -fash- (*fash*ion), -fit- (bene*fit*)

-fer- (root)

ORIGIN: Latin *ferre* (to bear or carry)
MEANING: To carry, bear, or yield
CONTEXT: "re*fer*"

A. In each of the italicized words below, underline the word parts that you have learned. Then, using your knowledge of the meanings of the word parts, circle the letter of the best meaning for the italicized word. (For some words there may be only one word part.)

1. *factitious* display of grief: a) honest b) touching c) made up d) designed to impress
2. *defer* treatment: a) diagnose b) finish c) undo d) carry over until later
3. find the *malefactor*: a) evildoer b) preacher c) messenger d) patient
4. *proffer* aid: a) delay b) apply for c) carry forward d) deny
5. in a *facile* manner: a) false b) easily done c) voluminous d) yielding
6. *efficacy* of prayers: a) piety b) transmission c) results d) requirements
7. *dismiss* the students: a) observe b) downgrade c) send away d) lecture to
8. *transfer* title to: a) attach b) give over c) explain d) clarify
9. to *vociferate* one's displeasure: a) hide b) shout c) write d) understand

B. REVIEW: Write one sentence for each of the following words. Each sentence must be complete enough to indicate the meaning of the vocabulary word through context clues and must not simply be an adaptation of a sentence in this book.

1. deficit 2. apparition 3. morality 4. grimace 5. vex
6. entrench 7. fruition 8. immaculate 9. divulge 10. vigil

Lesson 95

FABRICATE MOSAIC

fabricate (v) ('fab-ri-kāt)

ORIGIN: Latin *fabricat* (made)
MEANING: To make, devise, or invent
CONTEXT: "Amy *fabricated* the story about her mother's illness in order to cover up her laziness in school."
SYNONYMS: concoct, create, conceive, build, contrive, weave, compose, design
ANTONYM: demolish
OTHER FORM: fabrication (n.)

mosaic (n) (mō-'zā-ik)

ORIGIN: Latin *musivum* (artistic)
MEANING: A picture made of small pieces of inlaid stone or glass, or something resembling such a picture
CONTEXT: "The walls of the cathedral were decorated with *mosaics* depicting scenes from history."
SYNONYM: inlay
OTHER FORMS: mosaically (adv.), mosaicist (n.)

A. Circle the letters of the two words in each group that are most closely related in meaning.

1. a) condone b) concoct c) fabricate d) debate
2. a) national b) sensible c) vehement d) rational
3. a) wool b) fabrication c) creation d) concrete
4. a) mosaic b) commandment c) inlay d) aesthete
5. a) express b) transcend c) surpass d) transact
6. a) design b) investigation c) concrete d) mosaic

B. Supply the proper form of the most appropriate vocabulary word.

1. The worker inlaid a colorful ________________ into the floor of the foyer.
2. The judge would not accept the defendant's alibi since it became clear that it was merely a(n) ________________.
3. The *(size)* ________________ of the old redwood tree results from many encircling layers of growth.
4. A deep respect for the monarchy was ________________ in the minds of the people, and nothing could shake it.
5. The art store sold kits containing bits of colorful stones and glass with which to make ________________.

Lesson 96

scrutinize (v) (′skrüt-n-,īz)

ORIGIN: Latin *scrutari* (to search)
MEANING: To examine in detail with careful or critical attention
CONTEXT: "The police *scrutinized* the scene of the crime, looking for evidence that would identify the intruder."
SYNONYMS: study, inspect, analyze, examine
ANTONYMS: overlook, neglect
OTHER FORMS: scrutiny (n.), scrutinization (n.)

barb (n) (barb)

ORIGIN: Latin *barba* (beardlike projection)
MEANING: a sharp projection; hence, a biting or critical remark
CONTEXT: "I do not appreciate her *barbs* about my coffee; I know it's bad, but she doesn't have to remind me."
SYNONYMS: criticism, gibe, point, bristle, heckling

A. Circle the letter of the best meaning for each vocabulary word.

1. barb: a) interference b) criticism c) bribe d) barrel
2. scrutinize: a) stain b) scrape c) inspect d) heckle
3. mosaic: a) confusion b) inlay c) skeptic d) splashing
4. scrutiny: a) investigation b) bequest c) doubt d) eyeglass
5. fabrication: a) cloth b) crowd c) invention d) dictation

B. Supply the proper form of the most appropriate vocabulary word.

1. Remembering how he was outwitted in his last business deal, Mr. Cohen ________________ the fine print in the contract very carefully.
2. The next day at school Tom received several ________________ about his crucial fumble in the big game.
3. Because the witness had ________________ her sworn testimony, she was charged with perjury.
4. "On closer ________________, you will be able to see the cell wall," instructed the lab assistant as the students peered skeptically into the microscopes.
5. The ________________ made of jade and clear glass was Oriental in design and depicted a royal marriage.

Lesson 97

piecemeal (adj) ('pē-smēl)

ORIGIN: Middle English *pecemele*
MEANING: Done piece by piece
CONTEXT: "She turns in her work in such a *piecemeal* fashion that I'm never sure when I have it all."
SYNONYMS: gradual, fragmentary, little by little, step by step

contort (v) (kən-'to[ə]rt)

ORIGIN: Latin *con* (together) + *torquere* (to twist)
MEANING: To bend, twist, or draw out of shape
CONTEXT: "We watched spellbound as the yogi *contorted* himself into unbelievable positions."
SYNONYMS: distort, wrap, deform, disfigure, knot, writhe
ANTONYM: harmonize
OTHER FORMS: contortion (n.), contorted (adj.), contortionist (n.)

A. Circle the letter of the word that best completes each analogy.

1. eccentric: idiosyncratic : : ________: gradual
   a) piecemeal b) deficient c) inherent d) immaculate
2. bane: burden : : ________: writhing
   a) mosaic b) barb c) contortion d) fruition
3. fester: pacify : : ________: smile
   a) divulge b) fabricate c) grimace d) entrench
4. inherent: unnatural : : ________: sudden
   a) deficient b) immoral c) contorted d) piecemeal

B. Supply the proper form of the most appropriate vocabulary word.

1. Modern dance requires that one ________________ one's body into unusual positions.
2. The class ________________ the new teacher from the moment he stepped into the classroom, noticing even a small cigarette burn on the edge of his jacket.
3. "Your ________________ are in poor taste," retorted Ms. Walters to the student who was heckling her during the lecture.
4. Since the Goodmans could spare only weekends for work on the house, it was finished in ________________ fashion; consequently, some parts don't match others.

Lesson 98

per
spect

per- (prefix)

ORIGIN: Latin *per* (through)
MEANING: Through
CONTEXT: "*per*ceptive"

-spect- (root)

ORIGIN: Latin *specere* (to look at)
MEANING: To look, see
CONTEXT: "*spect*ator"
OTHER FORMS: -spic- (au*spic*ious), -spec- (*spec*imen)

A. In each of the italicized words below, underline the word parts that you have learned. Then, using your knowledge of the meanings of the word parts, circle the letter of the best meaning for the italicized word. (For some words there may be only one word part.)

1. unusual *spectacle:* a) letter b) sight c) procession d) position
2. child's *perplexity:* a) grasp b) inability to see through a situation c) games made at home d) simplicity
3. *persevered* during hardships: a) weakened b) remained strong throughout c) worked harder than usual d) fought criticism
4. *peruse* the book: a) publish b) take out c) look through d) purchase
5. jury's *perspective:* a) difficulty b) viewpoint c) thoroughness d) decision on a case
6. a local *referendum:* a) a recount b) a count of illegal votes c) an issue carried back to the people for a vote d) an election called at a certain time
7. lack of *perspicacity:* a) profuse sweat b) honesty c) ability to see through things d) ability to withstand hardship

B. REVIEW: Write one sentence for each of the following words. Each sentence must be complete enough to indicate the meaning of the vocabulary word through context clues and must not simply be an adaptation of a sentence in this book.

1. contort 2. deficit 3. mosaic 4. vantage 5. entrench
6. grimace 7. scrutinize 8. apparition 9. fabricate 10. alien

Lesson 99

articulate (adj) (är-ˈtik-yə-lət)

ORIGIN: Latin *articulatus* (distinct)
MEANING: Using language easily and fluently
CONTEXT: "The minister from England was an *articulate* speaker."
SYNONYMS: intelligible, fluent, enunciated
ANTONYMS: unintelligible, garbled
OTHER FORMS: articulation (n.), articulative (adj.), articulate (v.)

novice (n) (ˈnäv-əs)

ORIGIN: Latin *novicius* (new, inexperienced)
MEANING: One who is new to the circumstances in which he or she is placed
CONTEXT: "Although I have been playing golf for two years, I still consider myself a *novice*."
SYNONYMS: newcomer, beginner, initiate, apprentice
ANTONYM: expert

A. Circle the letter of the word that best completes each analogy.

1. timely: appropriate : : ______: fluent

   a) deficient b) piecemeal c) articulate d) inalienable

2. vehemence: ardor : : ______: beginner

   a) apparition b) barb c) novice d) scrutiny

3. geniality: graciousness : : ______: enunciation

   a) articulation b) contortionist c) novice d) deficiency

4. cravenness: fortitude : : ______: expert

   a) articulation b) novice c) fruition d) grimace

B. Supply the proper form of the most appropriate vocabulary word.

1. Since Mary Ellen was a(n) ______________ in the ballet company, she was not offered any leading roles; they traditionally went to more experienced dancers.
2. Peter ______________ the wiring diagram, examining each section very closely.
3. The worn upholstery was *(frazzled)* ______________ on the edges of the arm rests.
4. Mr. Robinson had difficulty in teaching the French class to ______________ the *r* sound properly.
5. I hope a semester in advanced public speaking will make you more ______________.

Lesson 100

abominable mainstay

mainstay (n) ('mān-stā)

ORIGIN: Old English *maegen* (strength) + *staeg* (stay)
MEANING: A chief support
CONTEXT: "Since her father's death, Jan has been the *mainstay* of the family."
SYNONYMS: strength, stay, prop, pillar, brace
ANTONYMS: weakness, liability

abominable (adj) (ə-'bȧm-[ə]-nə-bəl)

ORIGIN: Latin *abominari* (to deprecate as an ill omen)
MEANING: Causing or arousing hatred, extremely unpleasant
CONTEXT: "Protesting what they term *abominable* working conditions, the teachers at Jackson High School are on strike."
SYNONYMS: loathful, repugnant, detestable, hateful, disagreeable, unpleasant
ANTONYM: pleasing
OTHER FORMS: abomination (n.), abominate (v.), abominably (adv.)

A. Circle the letter of the best meaning for each vocabulary word.

1. mainstay: a) sail b) strength c) money d) tradition
2. abominable: a) snowy b) frank c) detestable d) abdominal
3. novice: a) visitor b) beginner c) urbanite d) skeptic
4. abomination: a) curse b) repugnance c) greed d) aborigine
5. articulate: a) fluent b) interesting c) enthusiastic d) hated

B. Supply the proper form of the most appropriate vocabulary word.

1. The regular recurrence of wars is a(n) ________________ aspect of history.
2. Joan Silverman, our star soccer player, is the ________________ of our otherwise inexperienced and weak team.
3. "Because we have many experienced people who have applied for this position, a(n) ________________ has little chance of getting the job," the personnel manager said.
4. The Swedish immigrants had trouble ________________ what they wanted to say.
5. Large alumni contributions were the ________________ of the college's finances.
6. "The mere idea of seeing that girl is ________________; I hate her," said Dan.

Lesson 101

improvise (v) (ˌim-prə-ˈvīz)

ORIGIN: Latin *improviso* (suddenly)
MEANING: To provide, invent, or arrange offhand or hastily
CONTEXT: "As darkness was falling fast, Jan realized that she could not make it to the lodge, so she *improvised* a shelter from fir branches."
SYNONYMS: extemporize, compose
ANTONYM: premeditate
OTHER FORMS: improviser (n.), improvisation (n.), improvisational (adj.)

impromptu (adj) (im-ˈpräm[p]-t[y]ü)

ORIGIN: Latin *in promptu* (in readiness)
MEANING: Done without previous preparation
CONTEXT: "The candidate gave an *impromptu* speech when a large crowd unexpectedly gathered in front of the hotel."
SYNONYMS: extemporaneous, offhand, unprepared, improvised
ANTONYMS: prepared, rehearsed

A. Circle the letter of the word that is neither a synonym nor an antonym of the vocabulary word.

1. improvise: a) rehearse b) premeditate c) frustrate d) extemporize
2. impromptu: a) careless b) unrehearsed c) prepared d) extemporaneous
3. mainstay: a) brace b) prop c) weakness d) postponement
4. improvisation: a) repertoire b) arrangement c) composition d) rehearsal
5. abominable: a) pleasing b) hateful c) loathful d) active

B. Supply the proper form of the most appropriate vocabulary word.

1. When the party began to drag, Debbie ________________ a medley of popular songs on the piano and quickly had everyone singing along.
2. During Mother's illness, Rick was the ________________ of our family, doing the cooking, cleaning, and washing for the entire family.
3. While she stood on stage with her classmates waiting to perform her part in the school play, Elaine's ________________ remarks brought laughter from the audience.
4. Having no time to purchase a costume for the Halloween party, Daniel ________________ one from an old tablecloth.
5. When David forgot his lines in the play, he ________________ well enough that the audience did not detect his error.

Lesson 102

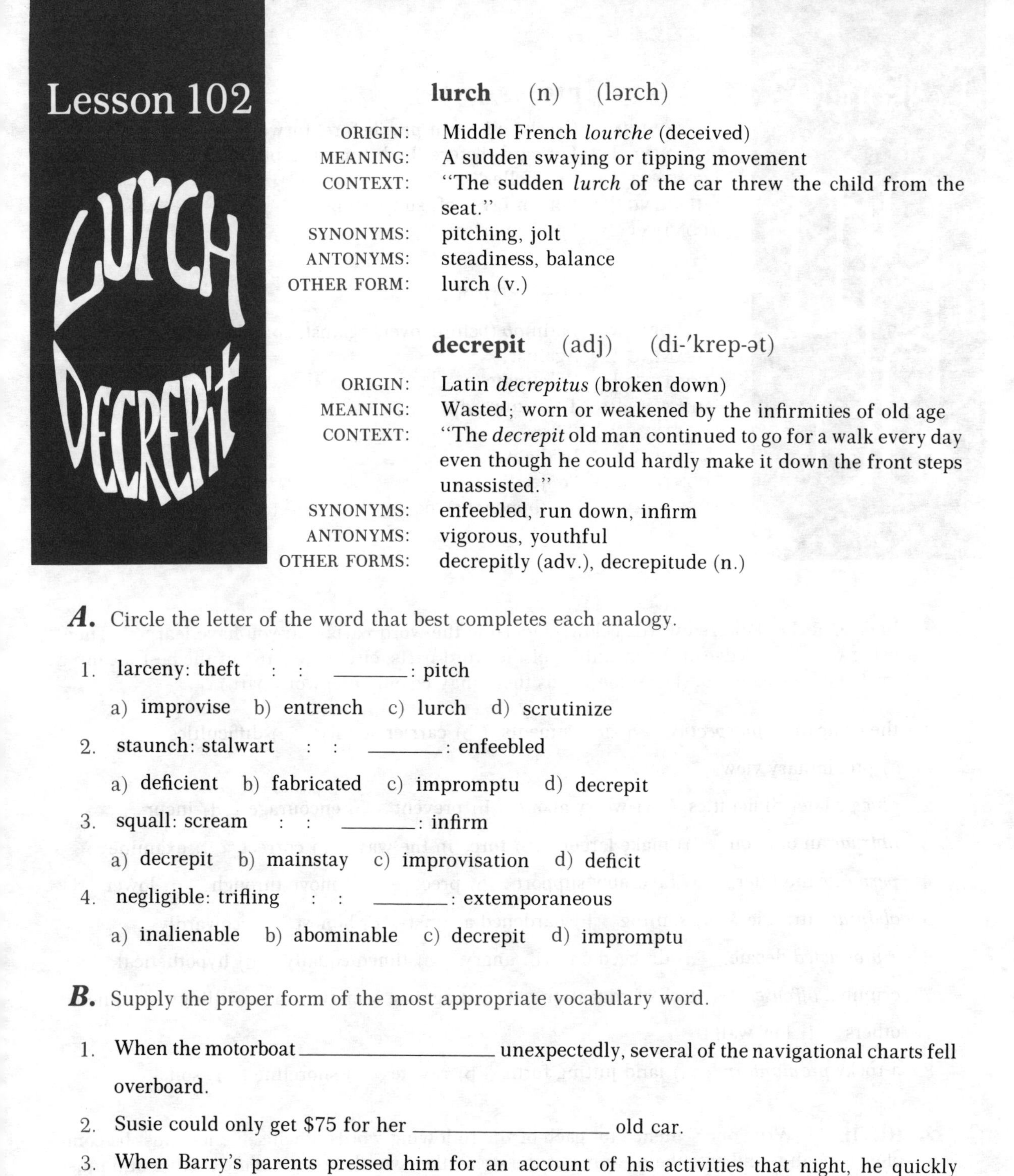

lurch (n) (lərch)

ORIGIN: Middle French *lourche* (deceived)
MEANING: A sudden swaying or tipping movement
CONTEXT: "The sudden *lurch* of the car threw the child from the seat."
SYNONYMS: pitching, jolt
ANTONYMS: steadiness, balance
OTHER FORM: lurch (v.)

decrepit (adj) (di-ˈkrep-ət)

ORIGIN: Latin *decrepitus* (broken down)
MEANING: Wasted; worn or weakened by the infirmities of old age
CONTEXT: "The *decrepit* old man continued to go for a walk every day even though he could hardly make it down the front steps unassisted."
SYNONYMS: enfeebled, run down, infirm
ANTONYMS: vigorous, youthful
OTHER FORMS: decrepitly (adv.), decrepitude (n.)

A. Circle the letter of the word that best completes each analogy.

1. larceny: theft : : _______: pitch

   a) improvise b) entrench c) lurch d) scrutinize

2. staunch: stalwart : : _______: enfeebled

   a) deficient b) fabricated c) impromptu d) decrepit

3. squall: scream : : _______: infirm

   a) decrepit b) mainstay c) improvisation d) deficit

4. negligible: trifling : : _______: extemporaneous

   a) inalienable b) abominable c) decrepit d) impromptu

B. Supply the proper form of the most appropriate vocabulary word.

1. When the motorboat __________________ unexpectedly, several of the navigational charts fell overboard.
2. Susie could only get $75 for her __________________ old car.
3. When Barry's parents pressed him for an account of his activities that night, he quickly *(invented)* __________________ a plausible story
4. Survivors of the crash said that the plane was making a routine landing when suddenly it gave a tremendous __________________ and nosed over into the swamp.

Lesson 103

pro ob

pro- (prefix)

ORIGIN: Greek and Latin *pro* (before, forward, forth, for)
MEANING 1: Forward; before (both time and place)
CONTEXT 1: "*pro*peller"
MEANING 2: For, in favor of, supporting
CONTEXT 2: "*pro*-American"

ob- (prefix)

ORIGIN: Latin *ob* (before, over, against, completely)
MEANING 1: Against
CONTEXT 1: "*ob*stinate"
MEANING 2: To or toward
CONTEXT 2: "*ob*ey"
MEANING 3: In the way
CONTEXT 3: "*ob*ject"
OTHER FORMS: op- (*op*ponent), oc- (*oc*clude), of- (*of*fer), o- (*o*mit)

A. In each of the italicized words below, underline the word parts that you have learned. Then, using your knowledge of the meanings of the word parts, circle the letter of the best meaning for the italicized word. (For some words there may be only one word part.)

1. the company's *prospectus:* a) investments b) carrier service c) difficulties d) preliminary view
2. *obviate* later difficulties: a) worry about b) prevent c) encourage d) incur
3. *obtrude* an opinion: a) make larger b) force in the way c) correct d) examine
4. *permeate* the filter: a) favorably support b) precede c) move through d) lower
5. *obdurate* attitude: a) smiling b) hardened against c) honest d) cowardly
6. a *protracted* debate: a) dragged on b) angry c) timed equally d) hypothetical
7. criminal *offense:* a) lack of education b) act against society c) unwillingness to help others d) low wall
8. a rocky *promontory:* a) land jutting forth b) ravine c) shoreline d) soil

B. REVIEW: Write one sentence for each of the following words. Each sentence must be complete enough to indicate the meaning of the vocabulary word through context clues and must not simply be an adaptation of a sentence in this book.

1. improvise 2. decrepit 3. innovation 4. lurch 5. impromptu
6. abominable 7. barb 8. deficit 9. articulate 10. mainstay

Lesson 104

PLACARD · UNOBTRUSIVE ·

placard (n) ('plak-ˌárd)

ORIGIN: Middle Dutch *placken* (to beat thin and flat)
MEANING: A written or printed notice to be posted in a public place
CONTEXT: "*Placards* were up all over town announcing the dates of the state fair."
SYNONYM: poster

unobtrusive (adj) (ˌən-əb-'trü-siv)

ORIGIN: Old English *un* (not) + Latin *obtrus* (thrust against)
MEANING: Not conspicuous or aggressive
CONTEXT: "Mr. Sims's *unobtrusive* manner kept many from realizing his influence in the community."
SYNONYMS: inconspicuous, unaggressive, modest, diffident, unassuming, unaspiring, unpretentious
ANTONYMS: vain, obtrusive, ostentatious, pretentious
OTHER FORMS: unobtrusiveness (n.), unobtrusively (adv.)

A. Circle the letter of the word that best completes each analogy.

1. saga: tale : : ______: poster
   a) glue b) placard c) picket d) stipulation
2. contingent: conditional : : ______: inconspicuous
   a) insurgent b) fluctuated c) unobtrusive d) stuporous
3. oscillate: vibrate : : ______: sway
   a) condone b) fray c) lurch d) appall

B. Supply the proper form of the most appropriate vocabulary word.

1. "When the train ____________ forward, I spilled coffee all over my coat," moaned a passenger to the conductor.
2. The ____________ building was torn down because it was a safety hazard.
3. ____________ posted all over town announced the arrival of the circus.
4. The woman, who was dressed in a gray suit, stood ____________ in the back row.
5. Carol had to ____________ her act for the audition since she had not had time to rehearse.
6. We printed the ____________ in bright green and orange ink in order to catch the crowd's attention.

Lesson 105

neurotic
acclaim

neurotic (adj) (n[y]u-'ràt-ik)

ORIGIN: Greek *neuron* (nerve)
MEANING: Emotionally unstable
CONTEXT: "Kathleen admits she is a little *neurotic* in being deathly afraid of heights."
SYNONYM: mentally disturbed
OTHER FORMS: neurosis (n.), neurotically (adv.)

acclaim (v) (ə-'klām)

ORIGIN: Latin *acclamare* (to shout)
MEANING: To salute with shouts of joy and approval; to announce with applause
CONTEXT: "The student body *acclaimed* the football team as their heroes at a special assembly."
SYNONYMS: applaud, praise, commend, salute
ANTONYMS: reject, disapprove, censure, deride, scorn
OTHER FORMS: acclamation (n.), acclaim (n.)

A. Circle the letter of the best meaning for each vocabulary word.

1. neurotic: a) spoiled b) angry c) unstable d) lucky
2. acclaim: a) tax b) scream c) condone d) applaud
3. decrepit: a) vigorous b) experienced c) enfeebled d) convalescent
4. acclamation: a) oath b) praise c) reprieve d) concoction
5. neurosis: a) attachment b) innovation c) mental disturbance d) memory
6. unobtrusive: a) amorous b) inconspicuous c) carefree d) unattainable

B. Supply the proper form of the most appropriate vocabulary word.

1. Returning from a tour of sixteen countries, the violinist was ________________ at a gala concert at Carnegie Hall.
2. The critics' ________________ of the Broadway play exhilarated the cast.
3. Whenever a dog merely passed by the front gate, the ________________ child, irrationally afraid of animals, began to shudder uncontrollably with fear.
4. The strikers carried ________________ protesting poor working conditions and salaries.
5. The psychologist worked with Harry to help him overcome his ________________ fear of water.
6. Laura is a(n) ________________ girl whose presence in a room is hardly even noticed.

Lesson 106

mediocre (adj) (ˌmēd-ē-ˈō-kər)

ORIGIN: Latin *mediocris* (halfway up the mountain)
MEANING: Moderate or ordinary ability, quality, or value
CONTEXT: "The choir's performance was *mediocre*—not actually bad, but not particularly inspiring either."
SYNONYMS: ordinary, average
ANTONYM: transcendent
OTHER FORM: mediocrity (n.)

crucial (adj) (ˈkrü-shəl)

ORIGIN: Latin *cruci* (cross) + *alis* (pertaining to)
MEANING: Involving a final and supreme decision; critical
CONTEXT: " 'Because the decision you make now will largely determine your future, it is a very *crucial* one,' Andy's father said."
SYNONYMS: momentous, vital, important, decisive
ANTONYM: irrelevant
OTHER FORMS: crucially (adv.), cruciality (n.)

A. Circle the letter of the word that best completes each analogy.

1. atrocious: wicked : : _______: momentous
   a) mediocre b) neurotic c) unobtrusive d) crucial
2. lenient: tolerant : : _______: unstable
   a) obtrusive b) neurotic c) crucial d) mediocre
3. grotesque: misshapen : : _______: average
   a) crucial b) mediocre c) neurotic d) obtrusive

B. Supply the proper form of the most appropriate vocabulary word.

1. The jostling of the crowd enabled the pickpocket to ________________ slip the man's wallet out of his back pocket and flee unnoticed.
2. When a basketball game is in "sudden death" overtime, every shot is ________________, since the outcome of the game can be determined by one basket.
3. Whenever the ________________ teenager is in a crowded room, he turns pale and begins to twitch uncontrollably.
4. Martin received a C on his essay because the teacher thought it was ________________.
5. "The next few hours will be ________________," stated Dr. Green solemnly. "They will determine whether the patient recovers or not."

Lesson 107

delectable
slur

delectable (adj) (di-ˈlek-tə-bəl)

ORIGIN: Latin *delectabil* (delightful)
MEANING: Highly pleasing, very enjoyable
CONTEXT: "The *delectable* dinner as well as the congenial guests made the evening extremely pleasant."
SYNONYMS: delightful, gratifying, luscious, delicious
ANTONYMS: repulsive, offensive
OTHER FORMS: delectability (n.), delectably (adv.)

slur (v) (slər)

ORIGIN: Probably Low German *slurrn* (to shuffle)
MEANING 1: To cast aspersions on, to slander; to slide over
CONTEXT 1: "The magazine withdrew the article that *slurred* the politician's good name."
MEANING 2: To speak indistinctly as a result of carelessness
CONTEXT 2: "Not able to articulate well, Joe *slurred* his words."
SYNONYMS: insult, belittle, disparage; garble
ANTONYMS: compliment; articulate

A. Circle the letter of the word that best completes each analogy.

1. vulnerable: exposed : : ________: delicious
   a) crucial b) delectable c) obtrusive d) atrocious
2. accost: confront : : ________: slander
   a) acclaim b) slur c) converge d) vex
3. pleasing: abominable : : ________: loathsome
   a) acclaim b) unobtrusive c) mediocre d) delectable

B. Supply the proper form of the most appropriate vocabulary word.

1. Ed nervously turned in his final exam, knowing this test would be ________ in determining his semester grade in chemistry.
2. On our trip through southern California, we stopped often to sample the ________ fruits on sale at roadside stands.
3. The movie star sued the newspaper that published a story ________ her name.
4. Ken talks so fast that he ________ his words unintelligibly.
5. Since the opening at the advertising agency requires someone with unusual talents, it is not surprising that the ________ candidate did not get the job.

Lesson 108

stamina (n) (ˈstam-ə-nə)

ORIGIN: Latin *stamen* (thread; namely, the life-threads spun by the Fates)
MEANING: Power to endure fatigue, disease, or privation
CONTEXT: "It took great *stamina* to face the continual hardships of pioneer life in early America."
SYNONYMS: fortitude, endurance, resistance, staying power, energy, vigor
ANTONYM: weakness

zenith (n) (ˈzē-nəth)

ORIGIN: Old Spanish *zenit*, modification of Arabic *samt* (way of the head)
MEANING: The highest point or culmination
CONTEXT: "The sun reached its *zenith* shortly before noon."
SYNONYMS: acme, apex, pinnacle, summit
ANTONYM: nadir

A. Circle the letter of the best meaning for each vocabulary word.

1. stamina: a) petals b) scheme c) endurance d) luck
2. zenith: a) heat b) lowest point c) highest point d) orbit
3. slur: a) insult b) capture c) slice d) fight back
4. stamina: a) fortitude b) fortune c) deprivation d) love
5. neurotic: a) prophetic b) emotionally unstable c) convalescent d) unhappy

B. Supply the proper form of the most appropriate vocabulary word.

1. Eva Dennis, an ambitious woman, reached the ________________ of her career quickly.
2. The frail man had an unbelievable amount of ________________.
3. I asked to borrow Don Jamison's recipe for the ________________ frozen dessert he served last night.
4. Running in a marathon requires training and ________________.
5. Many of the President's advisers suggested that he leave the White House while his popularity was at its ________________ rather than run for another term.
6. "The *Globe* has ________________ the integrity of our firm," commented the senior partner, referring to the disparaging editorial that appeared in the morning paper.

Lesson 109

symmetrical (adj) (sə-ˈme-tri-kəl)

ORIGIN: Greek *symmetria* (commensurate)
MEANING: Regular in form or arrangement of corresponding parts
CONTEXT: "The *symmetrical* landscaping adds a note of formality to the grounds."
SYNONYMS: balanced, same, similar
ANTONYMS: unbalanced, unlike, dissimilar
OTHER FORMS: symmetrically (adv.), symmetry (n.)

clout (v) (klaut)

ORIGIN: Old English *clut* (piece of cloth or metal)
MEANING: To strike, especially with the hand
CONTEXT: "Kevin *clouted* his sister with a rubber bat and sent her crying to her mother."
SYNONYMS: wallop, punch, cuff, hit

A. Circle the letter of the word that is neither a synonym nor an antonym of the vocabulary word.

1. symmetrical: a) unbalanced b) similar c) balanced d) straight
2. clout: a) hit b) strike c) punch d) argue
3. symmetry: a) balance b) similarity c) regularity d) arrangement
4. zenith: a) pinnacle b) nadir c) career d) culmination
5. clout: a) annihilate b) wallop c) punch d) hit
6. stamina: a) fortitude b) endurance c) energy d) size

B. Supply the proper form of the most appropriate vocabulary word.

1. The boxer ________________ his opponent on the chin.
2. The ________________ man felt his family were all against him, even though, in reality, they loved him.
3. Although we have two eyes, two cheeks, and two ears, the human face is usually not truly ________________.
4. When the sun reached its ________________, the inhabitants of the Spanish village closed their shops and slept through the heat.
5. Waving her arm excitedly, Sue accidentally ________________ Salvatore in the head.
6. ________________ in the mosaic was produced by balancing the design on both sides.

Lesson 110

PROVOCATION
CHASTE

provocation (n) (ˌpräv-ə-ˈkā-shən)

ORIGIN: Latin *provocatio* (a calling forth)
MEANING: Something that angers, irritates, or incites
CONTEXT: "Randy is ready to fight on the slightest *provocation.*"
SYNONYMS: irritation, aggravation, annoyance, incitement, vexation
ANTONYM: pacification
OTHER FORMS: provoke (v.), provocative (adj.), provocatively (adv.), provocativeness (n.)

chaste (adj) (chāst)

ORIGIN: Latin *castus* (pure)
MEANING: Pure in thought, speech, and action
CONTEXT: "Few prospectors were able to remain *chaste* after exposure to the sordid life in the Western mining towns in the 1850s."
SYNONYMS: modest, unsullied, virginal, pure
ANTONYMS: immoral, coarse
OTHER FORMS: chasteness (n.), chastity (n.), chastely (adv.)

A. Match each word with its synonym by writing the proper letter in the blank.

1. chaste ______ 2. provoke ______ 3. provocation ______
4. chastity ______ 5. symmetry ______ 6. clout ______

a) purity b) aggravate c) wallop d) vexation e) similarity f) pure

B. Supply the proper form of the most appropriate vocabulary word.

1. Ms. Edwards, apparently without ______________, started yelling at the student and demanded that he leave the room immediately.
2. His reply to the question was ______________ since it determined the course of the negotiations.
3. The two sides of the handmade sweater were not ______________; the left side hung a bit longer than the right.
4. ______________ maidens called Vestal Virgins kept constant vigil in the Roman temples.
5. White is a color that symbolizes ______________.
6. Ms. Lang's stimulating questions ______________ a heated discussion that lasted until after the bell rang.
7. The speaker from the defense department was constantly interrupted by *(heckling)* ______________ from the audience.

Lesson 111

component (n) (kəm-ˈpō-nənt)

ORIGIN: Latin *componere* (to put together)
MEANING: A part or element of something else
CONTEXT: "Most congregations believe that music is a valuable *component* of a service."
SYNONYMS: ingredient, constituent, factor
ANTONYM: whole

thwart (v) (thwȯ[ə]rt)

ORIGIN: Old Norse *thvert* (transverse)
MEANING: To prevent a purpose or plan from being accomplished
CONTEXT: "My plan of going to Memphis for the concert was *thwarted* when my father had to work overtime."
SYNONYMS: forestall, frustrate, hinder, obstruct, block, oppose
ANTONYMS: support, encourage

A. Circle the letter of the word that best completes each analogy.

1. join: converge : : ________: frustrate
   a) clout b) thwart c) provoke d) slur
2. moral: virtuous : : ________: part
   a) provocation b) symmetry c) component d) stamina
3. clout: strike : : ________: forestall
   a) thwart b) acclaim c) lurch d) grimace
4. immaculate: spotless : : ________: pure
   a) chaste b) delectable c) crucial d) mediocre

B. Supply the proper form of the most appropriate vocabulary word.

1. Our plans to hold a garage sale last Saturday were ________________ by bad weather.
2. Our stereo system has ________________ that can be arranged in any way we like.
3. The foreign leaders announced that they considered our establishment of missile bases on their border a(n) ________________ action that could lead to war.
4. The advance of the enemy forces was ________________ by our counterattack.
5. There are usually many ________________ in a short-wave radio kit.

mono- (prefix)

ORIGIN: Greek *monos* (alone)
MEANING: One, single, alone
CONTEXT: "*mono*plane"

uni- (prefix)

ORIGIN: Latin *unis* (one)
MEANING: One, single
CONTEXT: "*uni*ted"
NOTE: Do not confuse *uni-* with *un-*, which means "not" as in *un*attractive.

Sarah Frank

A. In each of the italicized words below, underline the word parts that you have learned. Then, using your knowledge of the meanings of the word parts, circle the letter of the best meaning for the italicized word. (For some words there may be only one word part.)

1. *seductive* smile: a) silly b) luring c) forced d) sympathetic
2. *monotonous* voices: a) loud b) many c) single-toned d) kind
3. a *unicorn:* a) funny trick b) one-horned animal c) vegetable d) goddess
4. president's *predecessor:* a) enemy b) advisor c) former occupant of office d) person in charge of protocol
5. a glass *monocle:* a) mirror b) support c) single eyeglass d) clasp
6. *conspicuous* placard: a) sketched from memory b) obvious to the eye c) crooked d) carried by several people
7. *unite* forces: a) sabotage b) lead c) give service to d) combine into one
8. deliver an *obloquy:* a) package b) speech against someone c) baby d) note

B. REVIEW: Write one sentence for each of the following words. Each sentence must be complete enough to indicate the meaning of the vocabulary word through context clues and must not simply be an adaptation of a sentence in this book.

1. symmetrical 2. thwart 3. delectable 4. clout 5. component
6. placard 7. zenith 8. mediocre 9. provocation 10. stamina

Lesson 113

constrain (v) (kən-ˈstrān)

ORIGIN: Latin *constringere* (to constrict)
MEANING: To hold back, to restrain, to force or compel
CONTEXT: "The opinion of the majority of the group *constrained* him from carrying out his rash plans."
SYNONYMS: check, curb, restrain, confine, repress
ANTONYMS: free, release, liberate, emancipate
OTHER FORM: constraint (n.)

tentative (adj) (ˈtent-ət-iv)

ORIGIN: Latin *tentare* (to feel, to try)
MEANING: Not worked out fully or developed
CONTEXT: "This is only a *tentative* report on the balloting because all precincts have not finished counting."
SYNONYMS: provisional, temporary
ANTONYM: final
OTHER FORMS: tentatively (adv.), tentativeness (n.)

A. Circle the letter of the best meaning for each vocabulary word.

1. tentative: a) slanted b) loose c) provisional d) improbable
2. tentatively: a) insensitively b) calmly c) slowly d) provisionally
3. thwart: a) free b) hinder c) clout d) argue
4. component: a) machine b) part c) answer d) comparison
5. constrain: a) travel b) tempt c) confine d) finish

B. Supply the proper form of the most appropriate vocabulary word.

1. The high walls along the river bank __________________ the rising flood waters.
2. Most teenagers are not permitted to run their lives without some __________________ from their parents.
3. Arrangements for hiring the "Electric Grape" to play at the spring dance are only __________________; the group hasn't signed a contract yet.
4. The bank robbery was __________________ by an off-duty police officer.
5. The two companies have drawn up a(n) __________________ outline of their merger plan, which will undoubtedly be altered before it becomes final.
6. Although Paul needed to replace a part in the engine, __________________ for a 1928 Bentley are difficult to find.

Lesson 114

undermine (v) (ˌən-dər-ˈmīn)

ORIGIN: Latin *infra* (below or under) + *minerale* (mine)
MEANING: To weaken by degrees; to attack by secret, indirect, or underhanded methods
CONTEXT: "The trust people have in the integrity of their elected officials is being *undermined* by false propaganda."
SYNONYMS: subvert, impair, sap
ANTONYMS: buttress, fortify
OTHER FORMS: underminingly (adv.), underminer (n.)

convene (v) (kən-ˈvēn)

ORIGIN: Latin *convenire* (to come together)
MEANING: To come together, usually for some public purpose
CONTEXT: "The board will *convene* in City Hall on Monday to discuss the proposed sales tax increase."
SYNONYMS: meet, congregate, collect, gather, assemble
ANTONYM: disperse
OTHER FORMS: convention (n.), convenable (adj.)

A. Circle the letter of the word that best completes each analogy.

1. decipher: interpret : : ______: assemble
   a) constrain b) thwart c) convene d) undermine
2. vex: irk : : ______: impair
   a) provoke b) undermine c) clout d) constrain
3. farce: travesty : : ______: meeting
   a) convention b) zenith c) provocation d) component

B. Supply the proper form of the most appropriate vocabulary word.

1. "Student Council will ______________ at 8 A.M. on Tuesday morning. All representatives please be present," announced Joe over the loudspeaker.
2. Since Lynn had not thought much about a career, her plans to major in botany in college were only ______________.
3. The psychological torture inflicted on the prisoners ______________ their loyalty to one another.
4. Michelangelo painted the Sistine Ceiling in a(n) *(gradual)* ______________ manner.
5. Although the Congress ______________ only twice a year, each assembly sits in session for several months.

inverse (adj) (in-ˈvərs)

ORIGIN: Latin *inversus* (turned inside out)
MEANING: Reversed or opposite in position, nature, or direction
CONTEXT: "It was surprising that so young a child could arrange the numbers in *inverse* order."
SYNONYMS: reverse, opposite
ANTONYM: direct
OTHER FORMS: inversion (n.), inversely (adv.), invert (v.)

spat (n) (spat)

ORIGIN: Unknown
MEANING: A brief, petty quarrel
CONTEXT: "Although the strong-willed friends argued often, their *spats* never lasted long."
SYNONYMS: argument, quarrel
OTHER FORM: spats (n. pl. meaning "a leather piece covering the ankle and instep")

A. Circle the letter of the word that best completes each analogy.

1. gist: essence : : ______: opposite
   a) inverse b) convention c) component d) fortitude
2. apparition: specter : : ______: quarrel
   a) spat b) clout c) inversion d) stamina
3. divulge: disclose : : ______: subvert
   a) invert b) undermine c) clout d) divulge

B. Supply the proper form of the most appropriate vocabulary word.

1. Rumors of the professor's sympathy with the radicals ______________ his respected position on the faculty.
2. Because we dislike quarrels, we settle our ______________ quickly.
3. Most ______________ between husband and wife are about money, but a carefully drawn up budget will prevent many arguments.
4. "My A in geometry is ______________," Pam told her parents. "I still have to take that awful final exam."
5. The teacher pointed out that in English, questions are usually phrased in ______________ word order, with the verb preceding the subject.

Lesson 116

SUBSIST OBTUSE

subsist (v) (səb-'sist)

ORIGIN: Latin *subsistere* (to remain)
MEANING: To exist; to remain alive
CONTEXT: "Many people in the United States today *subsist* on a grossly inadequate diet."
SYNONYMS: live, exist
ANTONYM: die
OTHER FORM: subsistence (n. or adj. meaning both "existence" and "means of keeping alive")

obtuse (adj) (ȧb-'t[y]üs)

ORIGIN: Latin *obtusus* (dulled)
MEANING: Not quick or alert in perception, feeling, or intellect
CONTEXT: "The boy did not realize his *obtuse* remarks had hurt the girl's feelings."
SYNONYMS: dull, insensitive, blunt, impassive, imperceptive
ANTONYMS: imaginative, acute, sensitive
OTHER FORMS: obtusely (adv.), obtuseness (n.)

A. Circle the letter of the best meaning for each vocabulary word.

1. subsist: a) lower b) deprive c) live d) question
2. obtuse: a) slanted b) insensitive c) heavy d) gloomy
3. convene: a) disperse b) free c) assemble d) imprison
4. subsistence: a) nutrition b) existence c) alertness d) substance
5. inversion: a) revenge b) answer c) wetness d) reversal

B. Supply the proper form of the most appropriate vocabulary word.

1. If we reverse the order of the letters, possibly the ________________ will help us decipher the message.
2. On the endurance hike, Charlie had to ________________ on cold beans and dried beef.
3. Laughing loudly, Josie made no attempt to ________________ her happiness.
4. The crotchety man's ________________ remark deeply offended the sensitive child.
5. The children's ________________ over who would wash the dishes annoyed their father.
6. The Council on Poverty defined the ________________ level as an annual income of $4,000 to $6,000, depending upon the state.

Lesson 117

INVALUABLE

invaluable (adj) (in-'val-yə-[wə]-bəl)

ORIGIN: Latin *in* (not) + *valere* (be worth)
MEANING: Valued beyond estimation
CONTEXT: "A good dictionary is *invaluable* to a student."
SYNONYMS: precious, priceless, costly
ANTONYM: worthless
OTHER FORMS: invaluableness (n.), invaluably (adv.)

annul (v) (ə-'nəl)

ORIGIN: Latin *ad* (toward) + *nullus* (not any)
MEANING: To make inoperative; to declare legally void
CONTEXT: "The law was *annulled* by the council."
SYNONYMS: nullify, invalidate, cancel, counteract
ANTONYM: validate
OTHER FORM: annulment (n.)

A. Circle the letter of the word that best completes each analogy.

1. craven: timorous : : ______: precious

   a) inverse b) obtuse c) invaluable d) chaste

2. immaculate: squalid : : ______: sensitive

   a) inverse b) invaluable c) obtuse d) tentative

3. inherent: intrinsic : : ______: opposite

   a) inverse b) tentative c) invaluable d) obtuse

B. Supply the proper form of the most appropriate vocabulary word.

1. My attorney can give you ________________ advice on how to constrain the city government from cutting down the trees in front of your home.
2. When Juan eloped without his parent's approval, they took steps to ________________ the marriage.
3. The teacher complained that the class was too ________________ to understand the finer aspects of the symbolism in Blake's poetry.
4. The young couple's marriage was ________________ when it was learned they were not of age.

Lesson 118

travail·deduce

travail (n) ('trav-āl)

ORIGIN: Vulgar Latin *tripaliare* (to torture)
MEANING: Hard work involving pain and suffering
CONTEXT: "The popular candidate reminisced about the *travails* of campaigning."
SYNONYMS: labor, anguish, toil

deduce (v) (di-'d[y]üs)

ORIGIN: Latin *deducere* (to lead down)
MEANING: To draw a conclusion from something assumed or known
CONTEXT: "From the evidence he was able to find, the detective *deduced* that the murderer was familiar with the house and grounds."
SYNONYMS: infer, conclude
OTHER FORMS: deducibly (adv.), deducibility (n.), deductible (adj., also meaning "subtractable"), deduction (n., also meaning "a decrease")

A. Circle the letter of the word that best completes each analogy.

1. contort: disfigure : : ______: infer
   a) deduce b) subsist c) convene d) invert
2. piecemeal: sudden : : ______: sensitive
   a) obtuse b) invaluable c) inverse d) tentative
3. novice: beginner : : ______: labor
   a) subsistence b) spat c) annulment d) travail
4. improvise: rehearse : : ______: validate
   a) undermine b) annul c) subsist d) constrain

B. Supply the proper form of the most appropriate vocabulary word.

1. The ______________ of working on the chain gang weakened the convict.
2. The judge's conclusion was not logically ______________ from the testimony.
3. The ______________ of surgery is quickly forgotten once the patient begins to recuperate.
4. Even though the conclusion was hastily reached, the ______________ was correct.
5. Barbara ______________ on grapefruit, cottage cheese, and vitamin pills in her effort to lose weight quickly.

Lesson 119

PARABLE SUBSIDE

subside (v) (səb-ˈsīd)

ORIGIN: Latin *subsidere* (to sit, to settle)
MEANING: To sink to a lower level, to become quiet
CONTEXT: "As the teacher entered the room, the loud laughter *subsided* and soon stopped entirely."
SYNONYMS: decline, diminish, lessen, wane, abate
ANTONYMS: rise, increase
OTHER FORM: subsidence (n.)

parable (n) (ˈpar-ə-bəl)

ORIGIN: Greek *parabole* (comparison)
MEANING: A short allegorical story designed to convey some truth, moral lesson, or religious principle
CONTEXT: "The teacher told a *parable* about a young man who squandered his father's money."
SYNONYM: allegory
OTHER FORM: parabolic (adj.)

A. Circle the letter of the word that best completes each analogy.

1. lurch: pitch : : ______: diminish

   a) convene b) subsist c) subside d) annul

2. hallucination: illusion : : ______: allegory

   a) travail b) chastity c) parable d) component

3. slur: belittlement : : ______: anguish

   a) subsistence b) constraint c) travail d) stamina

4. acclaim: applaud : : ______: live

   a) deduce b) travail c) annul d) subsist

B. Supply the proper form of the most appropriate vocabulary word.

1. Flushing deeply, Mr. Perez left the room until his anger ______________.
2. The speech was a series of ______________ taken from the other writings.
3. The ______________ of the raging flood waters was a relief to the farmers.
4. Since donations to charities and nonprofit organizations are not taxed by the federal government, they are ______________ from one's total income statement.
5. Because of its allegorical characters, the short story by Hawthorne was called a modern ______________.

Lesson 120

evade (v) (i-'vād)

ORIGIN: Latin *evadere* (to pass over, go out)
MEANING: To avoid doing something by cleverness
CONTEXT: "By leaving the party early, Roberto *evaded* the reporters who were pursuing him."
SYNONYMS: avoid, dodge, prevaricate, circumvent
ANTONYM: confront
OTHER FORMS: evadingly (adv.), evasion (n.), evasive (adj.)

substantive (adj) ('səb-stən-tiv)

ORIGIN: Latin *substanti* (standing under)
MEANING: Real; having substance; in a considerable amount
CONTEXT: "Anyone with a *substantive* complaint about his or her grade may see me after class."
SYNONYMS: actual, considerable
ANTONYMS: hallucinatory, negligible
OTHER FORMS: substantiveness (n.), substantial (adj.)

A. Circle the letter of the best meaning for each vocabulary word.

1. parable: a) lecture b) portion c) allegory d) realness
2. substantive: a) negligible b) actual c) equivocal d) likeable
3. evade: a) produce b) accost c) escape d) evict
4. evasion: a) prevarication b) invasion c) promise d) evolution
5. constrain: a) loosen b) curb c) think hard d) stress
6. substantial: a) mechanical b) handmade c) underground d) considerable

B. Supply the proper form of the most appropriate vocabulary word.

1. Not knowing the right answer, Juan tried to ________________ the question altogether.
2. After much preliminary small talk, the three negotiators settled down to discuss ________________ matters.
3. Gary hoped that by giving a(n) ________________ answer he could avoid revealing the truth to his parents.
4. Much to the speaker's chagrin, the heckling did not ________________; it grew louder and more vicious as he feebly tried to continue.
5. Because the students' complaint about the cafeteria food was ________________, the administration tried to correct the situation.

ANSWER KEY

1 A. 1. c 2. b 3. a 4. b 5. c
B. 1. bungle 2. bungle 3. surmised
4. surmised 5. bunglingly

2 A. 1. c 2. b 3. c 4. b 5. b
B. 1. cowered 2. surmised 3. fastidious
4. cowered 5. bungled

3 A. 1. c 2. c 3. a 4. a 5. b
B. 1. marital 2. marital 3. martial
4. fastidiousness 5. Martial 6. surmised

4 A. 1. c 2. b 3. a 4. c 5. c
B. 1. swabbed 2. marital 3. condone
4. cowered 5. swabs 6. condone

5 A. 1. b 2. c 3. d 4. b 5. d 6. b
B. 1. compatible 2. foyer 3. condone
4. compatibility 5. swabbed 6. foyer

6 A. 1. d 2. b 3. b 4. b
B. 1. dilemma 2. wrest 3. compatible
4. foyer 5. wrest

7 A. 1. c 2. b 3. c 4. b 5. a B. 1. wan
2. cowering 3. spinster 4. condoned

8 A. 1. d 2. b 3. d 4. a 5. d 6. d
B. 1. secreted 2. wan 3. vagrant
4. wrest 5. secrete

9 Exercise 1. b 2. d 3. b 4. c 5. d
6. b 7. d 8. b

10 A. 1. d 2. c 3. b 4. d 5. d
B. 1. vagrants 2. aesthetic
3. reprimanded 4. aesthetic 5. reprimand

11 A. 1. d 2. b 3. c 4. b 5. a 6. d
B. 1. equivocal 2. reprieve 3. reprimand
4. aesthetic 5. reprieve

12 A. 1. d 2. b 3. a 4. b 5. c 6. a
B. 1. rigor 2. gesticulated 3. reprieve
4. rigorous 5. gesticulations
6. gesticulations

13 A. 1. b 2. d 3. c 4. b 5. a
B. 1. pert 2. pertness 3. rigorous
4. consummated 5. aesthetic
6. gesticulations

14 A. 1. c 2. b 3. d 4. b 5. b 6. c
B. 1. plausible 2. convalesce 3. pert
4. plausibility 5. convalescence

15 A. 1. c 2. c 3. b 4. a 5. a 6. b
B. 1. cavalcade 2. dilemma
3. integration 4. plausibility 5. cavalcade

16 A. 1. b 2. b 3. d 4. d 5. a
B. 1. relinquish 2. credence
3. integrated 4. credible 5. cavalcade
6. relinquish

17 A. 1. ex- c 2. non- c 3. ex- c
4. ex- b 5. non- d 6. ex- c 7. ex- d
8. non- c 9. ef- b 10. non- b 11. e- c
12. es- c 13. non- b 14. non- b
15. ex- d

18 A. 1. d 2. d 3. d 4. d 5. d
B. reek 2. credence 3. reeked
4. exotic 5. relinquish

19 A. 1. c 2. a 3. c 4. d 5. a
B. 1. intimation 2. exhilarating 3. exotic
4. intimation 5. exhilarated 6. intimated

20 A. 1. c 2. c 3. c 4. c 5. b 6. b
B. 1. voluminous 2. slovenly
3. intimated 4. voluminous
5. exhilarating

21 A. 1. c 2. c 3. b 4. c 5. c 6. c
B. 1. voluminous 2. rampant
3. exuberant 4. exuberant 5. rampant

22 A. 1. com- c 2. con-, -junct- c
3. con- c 4. co- d 5. non- b
6. con- d 7. ex- b 8. -junct- b
9. -junct- b

23 A. 1. c 2. a 3. c 4. c 5. a 6. b
B. 1. concerted 2. exuberant 3. tawny
4. marital 5. concerted

24 A. 1. b 2. b 3. b 4. c 5. c 6. d
B. 1. context 2. perverse 3. concerted
4. perversity 5. context

25 A. 1. c 2. a 3. b 4. d
B. 1. gloated 2. concerted 3. laxness
4. lax

26 A. 1. -cept- d 2. -cap- c 3. con-, -flu- b
4. -cep- c 5. -flu- c 6. -cap- a
7. -flu- d 8. non- d 9. ef-, -flu- a
10. -junct- d

27 A. 1. c 2. d 3. d 4. d 5. d
B. 1. diverse 2. belittle 3. diverse
4. diversity 5. perverse

28 A. 1. c 2. c 3. a 4. a 5. d
B. 1. urbane 2. Urban 3. diversity
4. belittled 5. urbane

29 A. 1. e 2. f 3. b 4. a 5. d 6. c
B 1. buttress 2. postulate 3. urban
4. urbane 5. postulated 6. buttressed
7. equivocation

30 A. 1. b 2. b 3. a 4. d 5. d 6. b
B. 1. urbane 2. conglomerate
3. postulate 4. urchins 5. urchin
6. conglomerate